ANTIQUE & COLLECTIBLE TOYS

1870 — 1950

DAVID LONGEST

COLLECTOR BOOKS

A Division of Schroeder Publishing Co., Inc.

The current values in this book should be used only as a guide. They are not intended to set prices, which vary from one section of the country to another. Auction prices as well as dealer prices vary greatly and are affected by condition as well as demand. Neither the Author nor the Publisher assumes responsibility for any losses that might be incurred as a result of consulting this guide.

ON THE COVER:

Top Left, Victorian doll house, Excellent, $900.00; Mint, $1,900.00. Center, Victorian children's nursery blocks, Excellent, $300.00; Mint, $500.00. Top Right, General George Washington, Excellent, $800.00; Mint, $1,600.00. Bottom Left, celluloid policeman, Excellent, $200.00, Mint, $325.00. Bottom Right, horse drawn rolling wagon. Excellent, $600.00; Mint, $950.00

Searching For A Publisher?

We are always looking for knowledgeable people considered experts within their fields. If you feel that there is a real need for a book on your collectible subject and have a large comprehensive collection, contact us.

COLLECTOR BOOKS
P.O. BOX 3009
PADUCAH, KENTUCKY 42002-3009

COVER DESIGN BY BETH SUMMERS
BOOK DESIGN BY JOYCE CHERRY

Additional copies of this book may be ordered from:

Collector Books
P.O. Box 3009
Paducah, KY 42002-3009

@$24.95. Add $2.00 for postage and handling.

Copyright: David Longest, 1994

Printed by IMAGE GRAPHICS, INC., Paducah, Kentucky

∽ CONTENTS ∽

∽ ACKNOWLEDGMENTS ∽

Although this book may bear only one author's name, it is actually the product of many people whose toys and countless years of collecting have been brought together for a reunion of sorts in this volume. Without the kind support and enthusiasm of all the contributing collectors, this book could not have happened.

First, to Jane Anderson, I express my deepest thanks for allowing me to race through her house, play with her toys, and then photograph them all the while she was about to leave on a long trip to Alaska. I hope Alaska was great, Jane. Your toys sure are. Your lifelong love of children's playthings does us all great honor as you help preserve our past. Thank you for your kindness and hospitality.

Next, I have to thank the newest collector who was a contributor to this book, Glenn Edwards. Glenn has only been collecting for a couple of years, but he has already put together a first class collection of Howdy Doody and Warner Brothers character memorabilia. To an old and very good friend, I say thanks for letting me "shoot" your toys. To a budding new collector, I say welcome to the toy mania. The fever has struck.

It's hard to decide who to thank next. Two couples who share a tremendous love for toys and collecting are responsible for everything that this book is. Bill and Mary Furnish, and Elmer and Viola Reynolds have all been at this game of toy collecting for many decades. Their knowledge, experience, and general passion for old toys has had a tremendous influence upon my own toy interests and the way I collect. Since all of these people are folks to whom I will be forever indebted, I will thank them in alphabetical order.

Bill and Mary Furnish themselves are something to behold. The Furnishes have given a new twist to aging with grace. They get younger with every year. They smile more. I've known them for over a decade, and the more toys they find and friends they meet, the happier they get. Their world-class collection of toys already has a national reputation, and its scope is mind-boggling. Bill and Mary, I wish you many more great years of happy collecting. Through the knowledge, inspiration, and enthusiasm you have brought to countless younger collectors, you have served as teachers of toys. We all thank you for the fine education you have given us. May the old toys continue to appear on your doorstep.

Like the Tin Man and the Scarecrow who accompany Dorothy on her long journey to Oz, Elmer and Viola Reynolds have wandered down a lot of yellow brick roads with me. They were at my side when I purchased some of my own favorite toys, and we have shared many good times "on the hunt" for our collections. Elmer HAS to be the most enthusiastic toy collector in America. Elmer is always bubbling over with the joy that toys bring him. And Viola is always right there beside him, in her own sweet way demanding that Elmer pass up his impulses for "fun old junk" and instead seek out the toys in mint condition. Their fantastic collection of antique toys in mint condition is a credit to Viola's discipline and Elmer's tireless enthusiasm. One of my favorite lines from an old movie is "It has been an honor to know you." That is my sentiment exactly. I couldn't have done this book without you guys. I have done five books now, and so I thank you for the fifth time! You're the best in both people and toys!

Finally, for the first time, I get to thank my sweet wife, Ann. She has to put up with a lot of mess when one of these books is going together, but this time her toys became a part of one of my books. While I have put in the miles for my own Disneyana collecting, Ann has collected a wonderful sampling of Victorian and early twentieth century toys. So as a contributing collector, I thank you, Ann. As a friend who has been supportive and understanding of a husband who is just slightly a lunatic over toys, I thank you again. I owe you a lot more than one paragraph! And to my seven year old daughter, Claire, whose short height has allowed her more than once to find me a great toy hiding under the table, thanks for enjoying the crazy little world of toy collecting. This book has kept me away from a few too many Monopoly games and late night storybooks, but one day I hope you'll understand that I was doing what I really like to do. Besides, now that the book is finished, we can play all the Monopoly we want!

To Lisa Stroup and all the great folks at Collector Books in Paducah, Kentucky: I thank you for all the work you do that makes the books look great. You are greatly appreciated. And to Bill Schroeder, Jr., my publisher: thanks for committing to this book that many toy lovers everywhere will look through time and time again. Collector Books may be a most successful family business, but it's more than that — it's a friendly business. Your books have helped give all types of collectors the knowledge and feeling of legitimacy they deserve. I wouldn't trade you guys for the world! Thanks for ten great years of toy books together!

And to my readers, many who now own all five of my books on toys, thank you for your support, and kind words always extended when I run into you at auctions or toy shows. None of us is in this hobby alone, and if you will never forget it, I promise not to forget it either. You continually remind me that a fellow toy collector is never a stranger.

May this book help in the education of new toy collectors and bring satisfaction to the hearts of experienced ones. May it bring joy to all who love the toys that other children once loved.

I wish you happiness in your collecting!

—David Longest

Bill and Mary Furnish of Louisville, Kentucky, are collectors "extordinaire" in every sense of the word. Aside from joking about their incredibly eclectic taste in toy collecting, they collect just about anything. "We've been together for so long with the great fortune of having the same taste—or lack of it—with the same ideas about collecting. We can buy dolls together or toy trains together. A real 'he-man' doesn't buy dolls, or a lady doesn't buy trains. Well, we like to break that mold."

Their absolutely incredible collection of late 19th century toys is the photographic backbone of much of this book. Bill is proud to show visitors a beautiful celluloid Santa crib rattle and toy that was his very own as a child. It was with that toy that his love for all playful remembrances of childhood must have begun. The Furnishes, along with the Reynolds, own the extensive general collections of antique toys that are featured in this book.

Elmer and Viola Reynolds of Central Indiana have assembled one of the most comprehensive toy collections in the country over the past twenty years.

They began by collecting tin windup toys, but soon their passion spread to almost all areas of character items. Viola's special loves are the Rose O'Neill Kewpies and the countless collectibles inspired by her art. Growing up in the era of Saturday afternoon cowboy matinees, the Reynolds relive their own childhoods by collecting the cowboy western treasures of Hoppy, Gene Autry, and Roy Rogers.

Finally, through their long friendship with author David Longest, the Reynolds have continued to share his fever for old Disneyana, which now dominates their collection. As Elmer likes to say, "The real Happy Trails are those traveled in search of old toys!"

Jane Anderson has been an enthusiastic collector of antique and collectible toys for decades. Instead of concentrating on just one or two areas of antique toys, she simply collects examples of whatever she likes or the toys that strike her fancy. From antique board games to penny toys and windups, her collection is one that was drawn together by a true fondness and love for that which was once played with by the young and is now preserved by the young at heart. She seems to enjoy the excitement of collecting as much as the toys themselves. She is a toy collector with lots of toys, but even more charm!

Glenn Edwards is probably the newest collector who contributed toys to this book, but he certainly is one of the most enthusiastic. In the past three years he has put together an incredible collection of Warner Brothers Looney Tunes character toys and figurines and has also collected a wonderful sampling of great Howdy Dowdy items. Glenn is one of those collectors who really "connects" with the toys he collects. Howdy Dowdy and the Looney Tunes characters of Bugs Bunny, Elmer Fudd, Porky Pig and the gang were some of his childhood favorites. Instead of these characters simply being a part of his past... the toys make them a very important part of this present. He may be the newest collector in this book, but he might be the one having the most fun!

✑ PREFACE ✑

Welcome to the world of antique toys. This book is by no means the first or last word on toys. The world of collecting is vast, and the expanse of print media now keeping toy collectors informed is equally vast, so so I hope that this book will, at least, fill a niche on antique toy reference shelves. As of this writing no hardcover, full color, general line antique toy collecting book and price guide is on the market. I hope this book will be kept, used, and at the risk of sounding trite, loved. There is so much affection shared by lovers of antique toys. It is hoped that this full-color book will help to perpetuate it.

As has already been mentioned, it is not this book's intention to be the final word on toys. It is yet another addition to the already large printed bibliography of reference works on the subject. What is new here is the focus. This book presents a sampling of nearly 80 years of toy production, showing toys produced in the 1880's up through the 1950's. The first toys pictured here were played with by children whose parents were little when Abraham Lincoln was president. Our pictorial toy survey contains toys from the eras leading up to two World Wars, and the rebuilding "baby boomer" era of the late 1940's and early 1950's. The toys are grouped by subject matter and function. Vehicles and horse-drawn toys are grouped together, as are books and paper items. Character toys are grouped together as are games and puzzles. This grouping makes the book more useful as an identification or information reference.

The toys pictured in this volume were drawn from six private, unique, and very diverse collections. Some have never before been pictured in any book. They are presented here in full color. In many cases, an example of the toy existed in two or more collections, so often the best photographic example was chosen. This has also helped the book to present nearly all toys pictured in near mint to mint condition. Many of the toys presented here are examples of items in the best condition in which they will ever be found.

A total of eight principal contributing collectors and their collections went into the making of this book. This book presents toys collected by collectors with over 225 collective years of enthusiastic toy collecting experience. That's an impressive figure by anyone's standards.

For this book, we chose to shoot the wonderful old toys against primary colored backgrounds. This is a departure from the style of my previous books which utilized only blue backgrounds (and has now been copied by dozens of other publications in the industry) but it is hoped that it will add variety and visual interest to the layout. You be the judge.

✑ INTRODUCTION ✑

Like sailors on the open sea, the old "salts" of toy collecting among us would have to agree that in the past two decades we have weathered some stormy seas. Through recessions, inflation, fads, and fears, the toy collecting has gone on, but it has not always remained unaffected by outside forces. For my own part, I've been out there shopping for toys in a recession when money was very tight. No, the dealers didn't sell their toys for miniscule amounts or sacrifice them. They just didn't sell. Although people often make the comparison, the toy market is not like the stock market. When the toy market is "down", toy prices don't crash. Most toy dealers choose to ride out the storm and just keep prices steady. If toys don't sell, then they don't sell. The market does not get flooded in a panic to sell toys at any price. The dealers hold on, buying ensues, and sanity usually returns.

Novice collectors will quickly realize that good antique toys will always be "out there." The price that must be paid to acquire them may go up or down and vary greatly from dealer to dealer, but the toys will be there. I mention this only in response to the myth that gets circulated by old timers that the good toys just aren't out there anymore. That's hogwash! There are enough new dealers and new collectors joining the ranks daily to keep supplies fresh. If the "good stuff" doesn't seem to be out there anymore, then the good hunt isn't being undertaken. Finding great old toys takes patience and legwork, experience and time. The committed collector will always eventually find great toys. It's a fact of life in the antique world. What the collector can still find out there, and what he may have to pay for it are two of the subjects of this book.

New collectors may take one look through this book and be even more confused as to where to start collecting. This book represents a sampling of eight very different tastes. The best advice is — collect what you like. If you think old children's books and games smell musty and that's a turn off, then leave them alone! They do smell musty, but collectors who learn to love them also learn to look beyond that detraction.

Many people view their collections as compilations of objects of art. If we consider all aspects of quality toy design a creative art rather than an example of engineering and manufacture, then we can loosely classify toys as art. Most collectors of character toys have long considered examples of their toys simply extensions of the cartoonist's hand or filmmaker's eye. The drawing on paper or the image on film inspire the toy design, thus the final product is also art. The answer to "Where do I start?" or "What do I collect?" can only be explored in regard to personal taste. Collect what you think is beautiful, or fun, or what strikes a familiar, nostalgic chord within you.

Another myth about toy collectors is that they are all trying to recapture their childhoods by amassing the toys they never had. I would hate to think that this area of interest exists merely because of greed and unrequited childhood wants. It may be true for a few people, but I can't believe that most toy collectors lived unhappy, dreary "toy-less" childhoods. Nor can I believe that all mothers threw out their children's old toys on one shocking, psychologically traumatizing afternoon that the children can never blot from their memories. Let's get rid of the myth that most of us who love old toys are unsocialized nerds.

We collect antique toys because we love what we collect. It's more than something we just "like" because we seem to have a real fever or passion for it. Whatever the reason, something within us is fulfilled with each new toy we add to our collections. It would be ridiculous to assume that all the intelligent, colorful, enthusiastic, outgoing, charming, and basically happy adults who collect old toys have some common dark blot in their pasts. Toys are just fun to collect. It's as simple as that!

It is hoped that this book will be pulled off your shelf many times as you use it to build, maintain, or just reflect upon your own collection. There are probably many other books upon your reference shelf, and many others will follow after this one. But, I ask that you only hold this book up to two important, basic standards that my seven-year-old daughter (a first grader) requires of every book:

1. I hope you read it all the way through.
2. I hope you like the pictures.

❧ PRICE INFORMATION ❧

Toy prices are a fact of life for serious collectors. What a toy costs at a show or auction is extremely important because that alone may cause a collector to be elated at the bargain he has found, or frustrated because a toy is too expensive and out of his budget. Although most collectors would prefer not to constantly discuss prices or worry about what things cost, it is inevitable that honest considerations of whether or not a toy is worth the price about to be paid for it arise daily.

As nearly every book written on antique and collectible toys and their prices will suggest, the bottom line for price considerations must rest with the buyer. The seller of an antique toy can ask whatever he wants to for a toy. It may be far too high or much too low, but until he shoots a figure, no negotiation can begin. It is up to the buyer to determine whether he will pay the full amount, or consider making a counter-offer. Most dealers of general antiques and toys will consider an offer 10% to 20% less than their asking price a respectable offer for toys. Anything less than that might get you a fine toy at a great price; or it might make the dealer a little angry. Never ask a dealer his best price and then shoot him a toy offer significantly less than that. In a sense, you are making a liar out of him. If his best price is truly his best price, you owe him the respect of not making a counter offer. On the other hand, if you wish to keep the channels open for your wild card offer of a significantly lower price, don't ask what the dealer's bottom line is; simply look at the retail price on the toy and shoot him your figure. "Would you take $$$$" is always worth a try. A little buyer's etiquette, kindness, and a smile can often go a long way if a dealer has any "room" (comfortable margin of profit) left in the toy.

The pricing of the more than 800 toys pictured in this book is intended to give a ballpark figure of what the toy might cost currently. Every toy pictured in this work will certainly be found out on the open market at a higher than listed or lower than listed price often. It is not intended nor should this book be used to set toy prices on a national scale. It is not a definitive price setter; it is simply an added resource to be used by the interested collector.

What a toy is worth depends on how badly the collector wants it, and what his finances will allow him to pay for it. In each individual toy purchase, these are the two most important factors. Also relevant are the condition of the toy, its rarity, and, in some cases, the geographic area where the toy is being purchased. It has long been held that toy prices are highest on the East and West Coasts, and lower in the Midwest and South. This makes a little bit of sense because the cost of living also varies according to those geographic areas so obviously some variation of prices could be expected. The toy prices listed in this book are a reflection of auction realized listings, want ads, collector/owner purchase prices, frequently seen asking prices, and the general knowledge of seventeen years of collecting by this author. It is my hope that these prices make reasonable sense in any state, on any coast, to any given collector.

Two prices are listed for every toy. The first price listed is for the toy found in excellent condition. Excellent means the toy is still highly collectible, but does show minor signs of use that are not distracting. This is the attractive condition that most antique and collectible toys are found in. The second price listed is for that same toy in mint condition, meaning that it is as nearly new, pristine, and unused as an antique toy can be. If an original box is pictured with a toy, assume the price listed is for that toy with the box. If no box or original container is shown, assume that the price listed is for the toy only, as shown.

Remember, use this price guide as a springboard for your own research and negotiation in purchasing toys. It should not be used to set prices at the point of sale in the antique toy retail market.

CHAPTER ONE

❧ VICTORIAN AND EARLY TWENTIETH CENTURY TOYS ❧

When most people try to identify what is truly an antique toy, images of early china dolls in wicker carriages, paper lithographed dollhouses, early cast iron pull toys and rare paper boxed board games might come to mind. Nearly all of these items that are regarded as unquestionably antique come from the Victorian era or very early twentieth century. The toys from this period are those that might have been played with by our great-grandparents as children. These toys are now nearly four generations old.

If collectors consider that the passing of each generation from childhood to adulthood presents the opportunity for toys to be lost, discarded, given away to uncaring hands, or simply allowed to deteriorate in a damp basement or dirty attic, then the fact that the Victorian era toys pictured at length in this chapter have survived this dangerous "passing" four times makes their survival no less than a small miracle. It is the much loved toy that is saved or preserved to be handed down from one generation to the next, so the fact that any single toy has survived for four generations is quite impressive.

The antique toys presented in this chapter are typical of those that might be found in a museum, although all toys pictured here are actually from private collections. Although many of these toys have the look of being handmade because of the quality of workmanship, most are examples of items that were manufactured during the heyday of the Industrial Revolution when even mass produced toys were designed and assembled with great pride and attention to detail. It is the endearing quality of these very old toys that makes them so important to today's collectors. Aside from simply being fun, nostalgic playthings from the past, these significant toys are actual artifacts from the lives of children who lived nearly one hundred years ago. They are unique little pieces of history.

The bisque windup girl on the tricycle (Plate 1) is an incredible Victorian toy. Not only is the doll riding the three wheeled vehicle excellent in design and detail, the function of the toy is superior as her legs actually appear to "pedal" the front wheel. The seated boy with his writing slate of ceramic and wood construction shown in Plate 2 is also a wonderful example of pleasing Victorian era design and detail.

The unique little windup bisque doll pictured in Plate 3 bears the most unusual name AUTOPERIPATETIKOS. This beautiful little bisque doll with her dainty lace and wool coat and bonnet actually walks forward when wound. The craftsmanship and design on this toy is unsurpassed. She is a beautiful doll in her own right and she walks! The fantastic walking windup Turkish soldier pictured in Plate 4 is an excellent companion piece to the little walking girl doll of Plate 3.

Some of the most ancient looking and simplest of early toy designs are the turn of the century tin plate toys. These all have a common look since most have at least some paint flaking away from the shiny surface of the metal. Most of these tin plate toys are either rolling pull toys or windups with internal mechanisms. The walking woman in the hat shown in Plate 5 and the clown with bass drum rolling and walking toy pictured in Plate 6 are colorful examples of tin plate toys.

The baker and the chimney sweep mechanical action pull or platform toy pictured in Plate 9 is an incredible toy. Theorized by some toy experts to symbolize the struggle between good and evil, the chimney sweep and the baker seem to "face off" in this unique platform toy. Notice that on even this extremely well preserved example of the toy there is still some paint flaking. This is common on even the best examples of turn of the century tin plate toys. Notice here, also, that the paint is actually an enamel applied to the metal, unlike later lithographed toys that had their finishes stamped or printed onto the toy with inks and lacquers.

The embossed seaside sand pail pictured in Plate 12 is from the late 1800's and features a typical pose of Victorian children walking on the beach. The colors are more subtle on Victorian tin toys, and this particular pail gives a clear example of this. Another fine platform toy example of a tin plate item is the goat with a red saddle pull toy pictured in Plate 15.

Cast iron bell-ringer toys were extremely popular in the late Victorian era and into the early twentieth century. Many of these examples survive because they are virtually indestructible. Finding examples with all bells, ringers, wheels, and fine condition original paint is another matter. I can speak from experience here. My grandfather's original bell-ringer horse toy was played with by him as a child, then passed down to my mother. By the time I discovered the great old toy under a china cabinet in my grandmother's house, it was already nearly 70 years old. Then I began to play with it regularly for many years as one of the few toys my grandmother kept at her house on the farm. I played with it just like all of my other toys. I pushed it. I wrecked it. I ran into chair legs with it, and after all the abuse I gave it, it still came through with flying colors. I now cringe that I ever gave it such harsh treatment as a kid, but even with my roughness, it was no worse for the wear. These bell-ringers were built to last! (See Plates 16, 20 and 24).

Additional bell-ringer toys made of mixed metal construction (not solid cast iron) are pictured with their wondrously lustrous finishes in Plates 21 and 22. The three babies on the box wooden and bisque rolling pull toy with its mechanical action is a rare and interesting Victorian pull toy example.

Several fine paper and composition candy containers are also pictured in this chapter. Many of these have patriotic themes such as the two picturing George Washington (shown in Plates 27 and 28), Washington on a horse (pictured in Plate 20), an Uncle Sam Nodder pictured in Plate 33, and the Uncle Sam on the firecracker candy container pictured in Plate 34.

Two unusual and prized additions to any collection are the Alfonse (an early comic character) being pulled by a donkey cast iron pull toy (Plate 35) and the very rare Dog and Cat cast iron mechanical action pull toy pictured in Plate 36.

The three roly-poly toys pictured in Plates 41 and 42 are fine examples of wonderful color used on very simple toy designs. Roly poly toys became very popular during the Victorian era and can be found in a vast variety of shapes and sizes. Clowns and jesters (as pictured in these plates) are a common theme, as are policemen and early comic characters dating to the very early 1900's. (See the Happy Hooligan character roly poly pictured in Plate 43.)

One of the rarest toys pictured in this entire book is the Columbus Egg pictured in Plate 46. This incomparable rare piece was a toy souvenir of the "Columbus World's Fair - 1893" as is marked on the front of the toy. In celebration of the 400th anniversary of Columbus's discovery of America, the egg features the interesting action of an entire ship (the Santa Maria) popping up and unfolding out of the interior of the egg, which is, appropriately, painted red, white, and blue. Notice the delicate detail of the unfurled sails and even the tiny little crew members standing on the bow of the ship! This is an honestly remarkable toy.

The Gibbs Company manufactured wonderful wood and metal push and pull toys from around 1900. Often mistaken as toys manufactured by the Bliss Company which also produced fine quality paper lithographed toys, Gibbs toys more often than not feature a finely detailed horse as a part of their design. The horse and wagon pull toy pictured in Plate 49 features the very interesting action of horse legs set in motion when the rear wheel turns. Because the legs on each side of the toy move in opposition, the resulting action is quite pleasing, smooth, and realistic, much like the action of a pacing horse. The U. S. Mail Cart pictured in Plate 51 is an extremely beautiful example of all that is best in a Gibbs toy, just as the tiny pony cart by Gibbs pictured in Plate 52 is an example of fine realistic toy design.

Several excellent examples of Victorian era children's picture, storybook, and building blocks are pictured in this chapter. Blocks were considered educational toys during the Victorian era because they often contained stories, the alphabet, children's literature characters, or words with captions, and in addition, they could be used for building. Many of the very fine early examples feature absolutely stunning colorful lithography, and a few of the sets pictured in this chapter also "nest"; that is, blocks of graduated sizes fit one inside of the other so that the entire set of blocks can be stored inside the very largest block! The storybook blocks set pictured in Plate 55 was manufactured by McLoughlin Brothers around the turn of the century.

Another most exceptional Victorian toy pictured in this chapter is the Spear's Original Character Dolls shown in Plates 67 and 68. This fantastic English boxed set of cardboard dolls features glamorous children's clothes from 1900 that could be attached to the single doll body included with this set. The unusual thing about this toy is that the set contained one doll body but five different doll heads! Not only could the original owner change the clothes of the doll, she could actually change the doll's head!

Many of the bowling targets pictured in Plates 71 through 77 are prized paper collectibles. Victorian era targets have great potential for display since they are usually relatively large and quite strongly graphic in design. The finely lithographed and boxed block sets and the unique Bradley's Toy Village complete with ready to assemble cardboard houses (see Plates 81, and 83 through 86) are also remarkable paper playthings of the Victorian period.

Many of the boxed play and activity sets that are pictured near the end of the chapter still contain their original craft or art contents. These wonderfully lithographed boxes which contain educational pastimes for Victorian era children are excellent reminders of the days when childhood seemed less complex.

Without electric toys, without batteries, without dolls that talked or books that made weird sound effects, the Victorian child managed to survive. The toys of this era are most romantic in their innocent design, reminding us that busier and more technical toys of today are not necessarily better — just different. The toys of the early twentieth century pictured throughout this chapter take us back to the days of our grandparents' and great-grandparents' childhoods. The beautiful toys remain to remind us what their younger years were like. In the bright lithography, pleasing designs, and interesting action of these toys we can hear the laughter of happy and sunny days a hundred years ago.

PLATE 1. Girl on tricycle clockwork windup with pedaling legs. Bisque doll head, late 1800's. Cloth and velvet clothes on figure. Excellent, $3,000.00; Mint, $6,000.00.

PLATE 2. Boy at writing desk figure, late 1800's. He is dressed in ornate fabric costume, has bisque ceramic head, and holds a writing slate in his lap. Excellent, $800.00; Mint, $1,800.00.

PLATE 4. Walking windup Turkish soldier in uniform and turban. China head and hands, internal clockwork mechanism. Late 1800's. Exquisite detail on face and costuming. Excellent, $1,500.00; Mint, $3,000.00.

PLATE 3. Walking bisque doll, mid 19th century. Windup clockwork mechanism allows doll to walk. "Autoperipatetikos" has finely detailed original clothes. Fine detail on bisque head also. Excellent, $1,500.00; Mint, $3,000.00.

PLATE 5. Woman in hat is an unusual tin plate windup toy featuring moving action. Because paint on tin plate toys was applied to the hard metal, after nearly 100 years examples of these toys are usually found with some paint wear. Late 1800's to 1900. Excellent, $1,000.00; Mint, $2,000.00.

PLATE 6. Clown with bass drum clockwork tin windup, turn of the century. Features fun musical action and extremely bright colors of original paint. Excellent, $1,200.00; Mint, $2,500.00.

PLATE 7. Duck and ducklings painted tin plate windup toy, early 1900's. Paint on this example is about as near to mint as can ever be found. Duck chases ducklings as her wings flap. Excellent, $700.00; Mint, $1,300.00.

PLATE 8. Hook and ladder truck is of wood construction with rolling steel wheels. Features removable ladders and water bucket. Pull toy or momentum toy (you push it yourself) from around 1900. Excellent, $1,200.00; Mint, $2,500.00.

PLATE 10. Court jester on a stick Victorian rattle and bell toy. China and velvet, circa 1900. Excellent, $400.00; Mint, $900.00.

PLATE 9. The baker and the chimney sweep tin plate toy. Rolling of toy produces arm movements on both figures. Fine painted tin plate detailing. Late 1800's to very early 1900's. Excellent, $1,500.00; Mint, $2,000.00.

PLATE 11. China walking doll with original lace and net dress. Painted facial details, circa 1890's. Excellent, $800.00; Mint, $1,800.00.

PLATE 12. Tin lithographed and embossed Victorian seaside pail. Circa 1900. Excellent, $300.00; Mint, $500.00.

PLATE 13. Painted tin plate ram and sulky with driver windup toy. Paint is unusually complete on this example. Excellent, $1,200.00; Mint, $2,000.00.

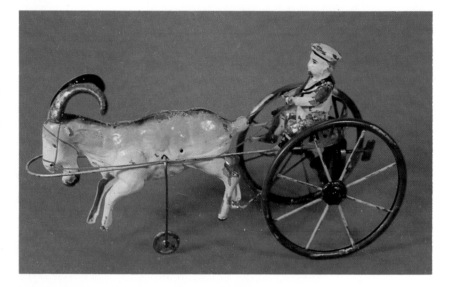

PLATE 14. Goat with ornate yoke pulling a wagon. Victorian tin plate windup. Excellent, $800.00; Mint, $1,700.00.

PLATE 15. Goat on platform early 1900's tin plate rolling pull toy. Excellent, $600.00; Mint, $1,200.00.

PLATE 16. Cast iron elephant bell-ringer pull toy with rolling wheels, circa early 1900's. Excellent, $700.00; Mint, $1,200.00.

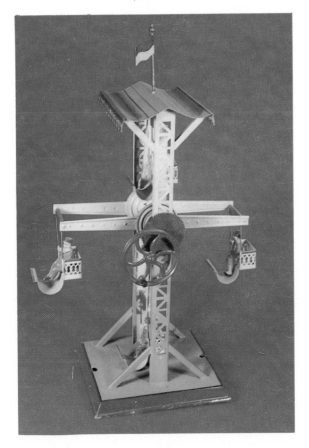

PLATE 17. Early 20th century crank action amusement park toy features four riders and four gondolas with paint in superior condition. Excellent, $900.00; Mint, $2,200.00.

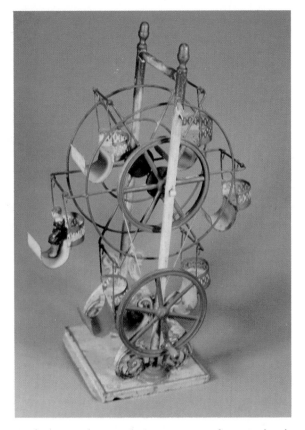

PLATE 19. Cable car crank action toy where cars travel up and down mountain. Early 20th century. Excellent, $600.00; Mint, $1,400.00.

PLATE 18. Turn of the century ferris wheel model toy with six colorful gondolas and crank. Excellent, $1,200.00; Mint, $2,700.00.

PLATE 20. Cast iron "see saw" type bell-ringer pull toy. Circa early 1900's. Excellent, $800.00; Mint, $1,400.00.

PLATE 21. Horse-race cast iron and metal bell-ringer toy boasting four separate bells. In astonishingly bright condition. Excellent, $800.00; Mint, $1,800.00.

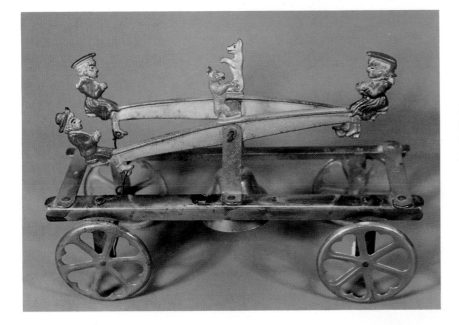

PLATE 22. Metal double see saw bell-ringer pull toy from the Victorian era. Excellent, $1,000.00; Mint, $2,000.00.

PLATE 23. Unusual three babies Victorian wood and china box pull toy. When the toy rolls or is pulled, the three dolls swivel in unison for pleasing action. Excellent, $1,200.00; Mint, $2,500.00.

PLATE 24. Eagle bell-ringer platform cast iron pull toy. Circa early 1900's. Excellent, $800.00; Mint, $1,500.00.

PLATE 25. Cast iron and metal fire fighters set complete with pumper and water wagons, and stationary ladder. Victorian era. Excellent, $2,000.00; Mint, $3,000.00.

PLATE 26. Late Victorian era Jack in the box type toy with colorful paper lithographed cards decorating the box. Excellent, $150.00; Mint, $300.00.

PLATE 27. George Washington chopping down the cherry tree colorful composition and paper candy container. Excellent, $500.00; Mint, $1,000.00.

PLATE 28. George Washington holding a cherry branch Victorian figure and candy container. Excellent, $300.00; Mint, $650.00.

PLATE 29. Foxy Grandpa riding a donkey composition rolling platform toy, circa early 1900's. Excellent, $1,000.00; Mint, $1,800.00.

PLATE 30. General George Washington riding a horse spectacular candy container and figural toy. Excellent, $800.00; Mint, $1,600.00.

PLATE 31. Mother fox holding baby fox papoose composition candy container. Superior paint detailing is shown on this example. Excellent, $400.00; Mint, $900.00.

PLATE 32. Paper composition rolling turkey pull toy containing smaller turkey bowling pins dressed as little clowns. Circa 1900's. An extremely rare set with this example shown in mint condition. Excellent, $4,000.00; Mint, $7,000.00.

PLATE 33. Uncle Sam paper composition nodder toy featuring exquisite colors. Excellent, $300.00; Mint, $600.00.

PLATE 34. Uncle Sam riding a firecracker container toy complete with movable head and double wick. Excellent, $500.00; Mint, $1,000.00.

PLATE 35. Alfonse cast iron pull toy with nodder head showing early comic character being pulled by donkey with "the nodders" molded on the side. Excellent, $1,200.00; Mint, $2,000.00.

PLATE 36. Dog and cat cast iron bellringer toy showing beautiful original paint. Toy features wonderful action when rolled along. Excellent, $1,200.00; Mint, $1,800.00.

PLATE 37. Set of turn of the century composition marionettes wearing exquisitely detailed original clothes. Each: Excellent, $350.00; Mint, $600.00.

PLATE 38. Set of five dolls and puppets used for Punch and Judy stories. Shown left to right are: The General, Judy, Baby, Punch, and the Judge. Each: Excellent, $200.00; Mint, $450.00.

PLATE 39. An impressive collection of turn of the century composition head hand puppets. Ranging from death as a skull to madams and policemen, these puppets represent an unusual cross section of life in early 1900's society. Twenty-six different puppets are shown here. Each: Excellent, $200.00; Mint, $450.00.

PLATE 41. Clown jester early 1900's composition roly-poly toy with dynamic painted features and colors. Excellent, $300.00; Mint, $650.00.

PLATE 40. Happy Hooligan riding on a dog ceramic, composition, and cloth candy container, circa early 1900's. Hooligan's head is removable. Excellent, $800.00; Mint, $1,700.00.

PLATE 42. Left: Keystone cop composition roly-poly toy. Excellent, $250.00; Mint, $500.00 Right: Billiken character composition roly-poly toy. Excellent, $200.00; Mint, $450.00.

PLATE 43. Happy Hooligan hand painted composition roly-poly toy, circa early 1900's. Excellent, $300.00; Mint, $500.00.

PLATE 44. Working cast iron and metal steam engine, all original paint and finishes. Excellent, $300.00; Mint, $600.00.

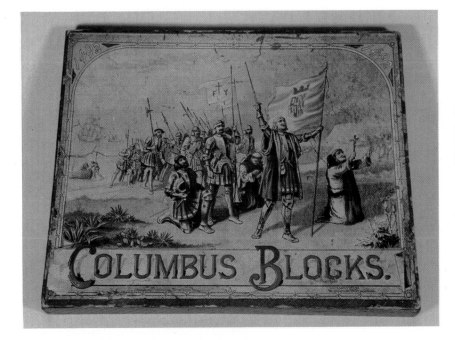

PLATE 45. Columbus Blocks boxed picture blocks set by McLoughlin Brothers, early 1900's. Excellent, $400.00; Mint, $700.00.

PLATE 46. Columbus egg. This unusual toy was a souvenir of the 1893 World's Fair Columbian exposition. Egg holds unfolding metal replica of the Santa Maria, complete with original sails, flags and crew! One of the rarest toys pictured in this book. Excellent, $3,000.00; Mint, $6,000.00.

PLATE 47. Hand carved clockwork wooden windup preacher at the pulpit. Circa 1880's to turn of the century. Probably manufactured by Ives. Excellent, $1,200.00; Mint, $2,500.00.

PLATE 48. Dancing dolls clockwork toy. Decal of young girl on front of box. Probably circa 1880's. Manufactured by Ives. Excellent, $1,200.00; Mint, $2,500.00.

PLATE 49. Horse pulling a wagon wood, cast iron and paper lithographed pull toy by Gibbs. Early 1900's. Excellent, $250.00; Mint, $450.00:

PLATE 50. Gibbs mechanical action pull toy with superior racing action. Early 20th century paper lithographed design. Excellent, $300.00; Mint, $600.00.

PLATE 51. Gibbs No. 27 U. S. Mail horse and wagon, early 1900's. When toy rolls along, horse's legs move back and forth with great action. Excellent, $300.00; Mint, $600.00.

PLATE 52. Gibbs small pony and cart pull toy, early 1900's, featuring mechanical leg action. Excellent, $200.00; Mint, $400.00.

PLATE 53. Tumbling acrobats gravity toy, early 1900's. Metal framework with composition clowns. Excellent, $700.00; Mint, $1,200.00.

PLATE 54. Fire engine picture puzzle, copyright 1887 by McLoughlin Brothers. Excellent, $300.00; Mint, $700.00.

PLATE 55. McLoughlin Brothers storybook nursery blocks, circa 1890's. These are nesting blocks which fit one inside of another. Excellent, $400.00; Mint, $800.00.

PLATE 56. Three 1890's children's paper lithographed wooden alphabet blocks. Excellent, $35.00 each; Mint, $50.00 each.

PLATE 57. Children's picture blocks from the early 1900's. Excellent, $30.00 each; Mint, $45.00 each.

PLATE 58. Children's nursery picture blocks from the early 1900's. Excellent, $30.00 each; Mint, $45.00 each.

PLATE 59. Animal soldier picture blocks, vertical edge shown featuring fine detailed lithography, circa early 1900's. Excellent, $75.00; Mint, $100.00 set.

PLATE 60. Victorian nursery blocks set with hollow wood and paper construction. Late 1800's to early 1900's. Excellent, $300.00; Mint, $500.00 set.

PLATE 61. Fancy solid wooden alphabet blocks, early 1900's. Excellent, $30.00; Mint, $50.00 set.

PLATE 62. Reverse of alphabet blocks shown in plate 61.

PLATE 63. Box of Pictures to Paint Victorian boxed children's painting set, manufactured by McLoughlin Brothers and copyright 1882. Excellent, $100.00; Mint, $200.00.

PLATE 64. Toy locomotive, tin and cast iron. From the Victorian era, probably around 1900. Excellent, $500.00; Mint, $900.00.

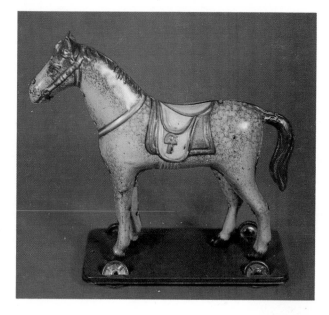

PLATE 65. Tin lithographed horse on rolling platform. All tin and metal construction. Excellent, $200.00; Mint, $450.00.

PLATE 66. Left: Wooly little bear figure, circa early 1900's. Excellent, $50.00; Mint, $100.00 Right: Cloth dog with glass eyes tiny rolling toy, circa 1900. Excellent, $125.00; Mint, $250.00.

PLATE 67. Spear's Original Character Dolls 1890's Victorian paper doll set. This gorgeous boxed set contains one doll body, various outfits and a fascinating assortment of interchangeable doll faces, as shown on box lid and in Plate 68. Excellent, $150.00; Mint, $300.00.

PLATE 68. Contents of Spear's Original Character Dolls box shown in Plate 67. This set was made in England.

PLATE 69. Drawing Made Easy, copyright 1887 boxed drawing set by McLoughlin Brothers of New York. Excellent, $75.00; Mint, $125.00.

PLATE 70. Drawing Made Easy graphed illustrations booklet and box. The object of this set was to reproduce a picture by copying the design one small box at a time.

PLATE 71. Palmer Cox Brownies characters bowling targets, copyright 1892. Figures in Plates 71 and 72 go together to make a set. Excellent, $300.00; Mint, $500.00 set.

PLATE 72. Palmer Cox Brownie character bowling targets, copyright 1892. Excellent, $300.00; Mint, $500.00 set.

PLATE 73. Palmer Cox Brownie character paper lithographed targets with wooden stands. Circa 1890's. Excellent, $250.00; Mint, $350.00 set.

PLATE 74. Early Punch and Judy and walking dog standup targets from a boxed set, circa early 1900's. Note the incredible detail of the early lithography. Excellent, $300.00; Mint, $450.00 set.

PLATE 75. Policeman and Hangman bowling targets, circa 1890's. Note the inclusion of such unusual characters as an angry cop and an executioner in a children's toy. Excellent, $150.00; Mint, $250.00 set.

PLATE 76. Three wood and paper lithographed bowling targets, circa 1890, from same set as pictured in Plate 75. Notice the inclusion of the odd smiling ghost figure. Excellent, $200.00; Mint, $400.00 set of 3.

PLATE 77. Set of three early 1900's targets from a game set. The cat on left is dressed as an old maid with the words "Miss Alla Lone" on her hat box. Also shown are Gentlemen Bear and Elephant. Excellent, $100.00; Mint, $200.00; not a complete set.

PLATE 78. Seneca spelling blocks, boxed set of alphabet blocks, 1890's. Excellent, $125.00; Mint, $225.00.

PLATE 80. Clown paperboard lithographed target complete with original rings, circa 1900. Excellent, $200.00; Mint, $400.00.

PLATE 79. Spinster Cat paper lithographed game target, early 1900's. Initials "PC" on her purse stand for Pussy Cat. Excellent, $50.00; Mint, $70.00.

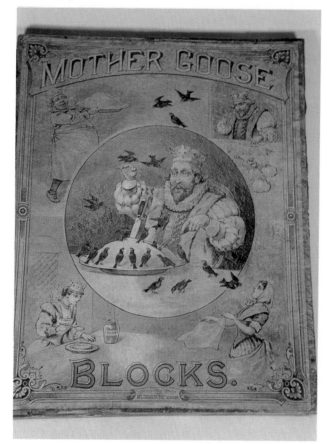

PLATE 81. Mother Goose blocks set with intricate lithography, copyright 1894 by McLoughlin Brothers of New York. Excellent, $200.00; Mint, $450.00.

PLATE 82. "Who Killed Cock Robin?" puzzle blocks boxed play set makes six pictures. Colorfully lithographed, this set was part of the Dean's Artistic Series, circa 1890's. Manufactured in England. Excellent, $200.00; Mint, $400.00.

PLATE 83. Bradley's Toy Village, manufactured by the Milton Bradley Company of Springfield, Massachusetts. Boxed component paper parts could be assembled to make a 3-D village. Excellent, $100.00; Mint, $200.00.

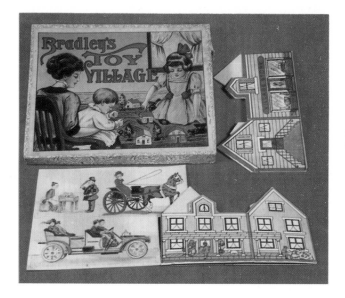

PLATE 84. Some of the pieces contained within the Bradley's Toy Village.

PLATE 85. Two buildings assembled from the earliest version of Milton Bradley's Toy Village, circa 1900. Shown here are a house with children playing and the village school. Excellent, $50.00; Mint, $100.00 pair.

PLATE 86. House and gambrel roofed mansion from the Bradley's Toy Village. Excellent, $50.00; Mint, $100.00 pair.

PLATE 87. Parker Brothers Cut Up Birds scroll picture puzzle, circa early 1900's. Many puzzles used terms such as "Cut Up" or "Dissected." Excellent, $100.00; Mint, $200.00.

PLATE 88. Flying steamship picture puzzle in the original box by McLoughlin Brothers of New York. From the early 1900's. Excellent, $200.00; Mint, $350.00.

PLATE 89. Simple Sewing Cards boxed play set manufactured by Milton Bradley of Springfield, Massachusetts. Excellent, $75.00; Mint, $125.00.

PLATE 90. Simple Sewing Cards by Milton Bradley showing original contents.

PLATE 91. Duplex Puzzle Picture featuring a single puzzle divided into two pictures. Circa early 1900's. Excellent, $75.00; Mint, $150.00.

PLATE 92. Drawing Teacher toy drawing set manufactured by the Milton Bradley Company of Springfield, Massachusetts. Excellent, $60.00; Mint, $90.00.

PLATE 93. Tin and metal action toy with full figure of boy on sled. Excellent, $500.00; Mint, $1,000.00.

PLATE 94. Tin and metal boy on sled action toy with near pristine paint on boy figure. Excellent, $500.00; Mint, $1,000.00.

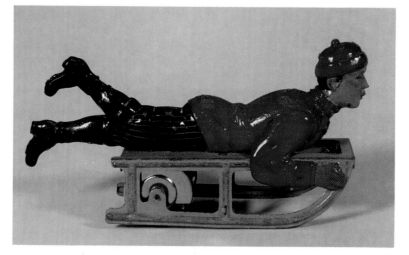

PLATE 95. Duo rooster, egg and rabbit detailed lithographed windup tin toy utilizing all the standard symbolic animals of Easter. By Lehmann. Excellent, $1,000.00; Mint, $1,700.00.

PLATE 96. Superbly lithographed mother mallard duck and ducklings in a basket windup toy, called "Quack-Quack," by Lehmann. Excellent, $400.00; Mint, $800.00.

PLATE 97. Lehmann Company lithographed tin windup lithographic sea lion with rolling, swimming action. Excellent, $600.00; Mint, $1,200.00.

PLATE 98. Old Hickory Building Blocks manufactured by Newton and Thompson Manufacturing Company of Brandon, Vermont. Complete set. Excellent, $50.00; Mint, $125.00 set, in box.

PLATE 99. Two embossed and brightly lithographed tin child's cups from around 1900. Left: Excellent, $40.00; Mint, $65.00. Right: Excellent, $75.00; Mint, $125.00.

PLATE 100. Mary and her little lamb child's colorfully lithographed tin tea tray. Circa 1895–1900. Excellent, $75.00; Mint, $125.00.

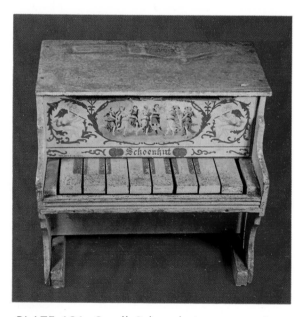

PLATE 101. Small Schoenhut nursery piano with gold paint trim, eight actual notes that play, and classical motif cherubs and dancing children. Excellent, $75.00; Mint, $200.00.

PLATE 102. ABC Simplex Typewriter "The Kindergarten Typewriter" with the box copy "Enough pleasure for two. You write me and I'll write you." Excellent, $60.00; Mint, $125.00.

PLATE 103. Richard Outcault character Buster Brown with his dog Tige. Shown here is early 1900's box only. Excellent, $100.00; Mint, $200.00.

PLATE 104. Boy's wooden tool chest manufactured by Bliss in the early 1900's. Excellent, $75.00; Mint, $150.00.

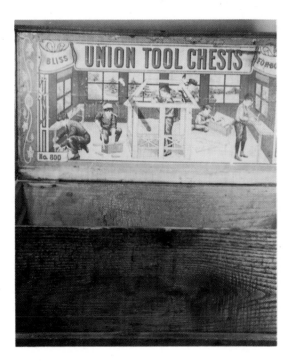

CHAPTER TWO

❧ TRANSPORTATION AND VEHICLE TOYS ❧

The human race's fascination with the wheel is evident in prehistoric art and artifacts. Our ancestors realized that the wheel and subsequent carts, wagons, and rolling vehicles made life much easier. As we consider how important horse drawn carriages, carts, and wagons were to our ancestors right up until the development of gas and steam driven vehicles, it comes as no surprise that these significant inventions would quickly find themselves depicted in children's toys.

The designs of good toys so often mirror the designs of everyday life, so it should come as no surprise that the horse pulling a cart or wagon was one of the most popular toy subjects one hundred years ago.

Certainly children like things that roll. Small vehicles that could be wound or simply pushed along, often referred to as "momentum", were extremely popular among children of both sexes. And it goes without a doubt that children love animals, and in particular horses. Add a horse to the front of a rolling wagon or cart and early toymakers had an instant hit with their tin windup, tin plate, cast iron, or metal horse and cart toys. These toys were not only fun to play with and push along, they included an animal design and they mirrored real life. That is why these early toys are also wonderful historical artifacts.

The tiny plate windup painted horse and cart pictured in Plate105 is an excellent example of a very early horse-drawn children's toy. The paint finish on this particular example is incredibly complete and bright, without the normal massive amounts of paint flaking. The horse on the platform rolling toy pictured in Plate 106 is another fine example of an early horse on wheels theme. The early tin double horse-drawn trolley dates from before the turn of the century and presents a wonderfully detailed embossed trolley design.

The horse and carriage momentum toy pictured in Plate 108 is an interesting example of a dapper prancing white horse pulling an unusual scoop shaped carriage. This design in particular lends itself well to actually transporting a doll or toy animal because of the openness of its carriage compartment. The horse with the rider pulling the blue carriage pictured in Plate 110 is both unusual and more ornate than many folk-designed tin plate horse and buggy toys.

The cast iron horse and wagon toys pictured in Plates 113 and 114 are beautiful examples of the detailing that can still be found on existing cast iron toys today. The Seventh Regiment Ambulance pictured in Plate 114 is a particularly striking example of cast iron design with its original paint and twin team of prancing horses. The two cast iron horse drawn fire pumpers pictured in Plates 119 and 120 show intricate mold design and detailing. Fire wagon teams and horse drawn fire fighting vehicles were popular themes for turn of the century cast iron toy manufacturers.

From the cast iron horse drawn wagons and carriages we move into the twentieth century with early automobiles and trucks. Just as soon as motorized vehicles appeared on the market in actual use, so did the wonderful tin and cast iron replicas of the early cars and trucks. The blue touring sedan of cast iron pictured in Plate 128 is a sharp design complete with spare tire on the back. Also worthy of mention for its unusual design is the cast iron truck Auto Express 548 pictured in Plate 130. This pickup truck with its original cream colored paint is also complete with its original cast iron driver inside. The wrecker and transport truck pictured in Plate 131 complete with working winch and flatbed platform trailer is also a most exceptional early vehicle. Another fine early cast iron auto example is the early roadster racer complete with speeding driver leaning into the wind, pictured in Plate 132.

The Andy Gump cast iron roadster pictured in Plate 138 is an interesting cross-over collectible manufactured by Arcade. Aside from being a desirable collectible among cast iron and vehicle collectors, it is also a greatly sought-after piece for early comic character toy collectors.

From cast iron, this pictorial chapter moves into the realm of tin windup vehicles. As the category of cast iron vehicles boasts very recognizable manufacturers such as Arcade, Barclay, Hubley, and Kenton as major toy manufacturers, so there are significant principal manufacturers among the tin windup toy makers at the beginning of the twentieth century. Lehmann toys, manufactured in Germany, are considered by most collectors to be the cream of the crop of early twentieth century windup vehicle toys. The tin lithography on the vehicles and on the interesting characters riding them is always superb. Consider the excellent detail on the Chimney Sweep and the Baker windup toy pictured in Plate 142. An interesting treatment of a popular folk theme, the characters on the vehicle themselves are as interesting as the vehicle that they are riding. And the Lehmann Motor Rad-cycle pictured in Plate 144 is not to be outdone since it features not only a tricycle vehicle driven by a rider in the front, but also a beautiful young lady riding in the wagon that is drawn behind it! This is an interesting and highly desirable Lehmann design. The Lehmann vehicle pictured in Plate 145 shows a close-up of the exquisite detailing found on the characters "driving" the windup toys manufactured by this company.

The Lehmann Dare Devil cart pulled by the zebra pictured in Plate 150 shows the wonderful coloring and clear details so typical of all Lehmann quality toys, and the OHO car in Plate 154, also by this company, shows a brilliant lithographed color combination with the bright green body of the windup vehicle and the driver wearing bright orange.

One of the most popular of all the Lehmann designs is the TUT TUT car pictured in Plate 155, so named because of the sound that the driver of this quaint little auto makes when he blows his horn. Aside from the great graphics and action of this toy, it is unusual because its driver figure and the vehicle itself are much larger than most of the Lehmann windup vehicles. The Lehmann ZIG ZAG rolling toy in Plate 158, patent date 1903, features dual drivers riding inside a rolling framework. This unusual design may have proven impractical for a real vehicle, but it made for a wonderful, odd toy design!

The Lehmann Balky Mule is one of the most common of all the windup toys manufactured by this company, but it features great character action and is shown with the original box in Plate 159. And the RUCK RUCK vehicle pictured in Plate 161 (also by Lehmann) once again shows an interesting color combination in the lithography of the car and driver.

The Marx orange roadster pictured in Plate 169 returns us to toys by American manufacturers. This particular example is in surprisingly mint condition and consequently shows the toy's original luster and fantastic lithographic detailing right down to the writing on the balloon tires!

The Junior Oil Tanker truck pictured in Plate 174 was manufactured by Ferdinand Strauss and shows clearly the extremely bright colors used on many of this company's toy vehicles. A similar design by a different company is the Dan-Dee Oil Truck pictured in Plate 175 which was manufactured by the J. Chein Company. The Fire Chief Car with windup mechanism and realistic sounding siren pictured in all of its bright red glory in Plate 180 was manufactured by Girard. And although the Hook and Ladder Truck shown with its original box in Plate 185 manufactured by Hubley, and the truck and trailer pictured in Plate 186 and manufactured by Courtland are both rather common vehicle examples, they are no less significant because of their popularity and familiarity by children of the day.

Several interesting and different train and steamship examples round out this chapter. The transportation vehicles presented in this chapter cover nearly 80 years of toy production. In every decade that these toys were produced, they served to mirror many of the actual vehicles used in real life during the same time period. What we today view as pure nostalgia and historical memorabilia of children's playthings were once played with as contemporary imitations of reality. We must never forget that today's Hot Wheels or Matchbox cars may be equally as rare and treasured in a hundred years as Arcade cast iron toys or Lehmann windups are today.

Little cars, little trucks, little horses and wagons. As long as there are little children to play with them, and keep them, there will eventually be adult hands to reach back and desire to preserve them for future generations to come. In our own way, we all want our own childhoods to be remembered, to be significant. By preserving our toys, we insure that our grand days of winding up or rolling little cars along the sidewalk or down the driveway won't be forgotten.

Little cars, little trucks, and little horses and wagons. Let's hope that they will always be rolling around!

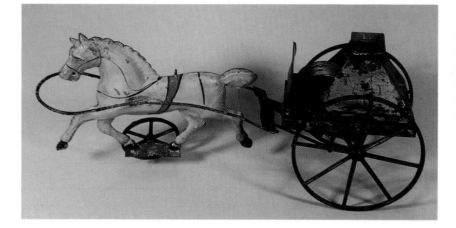

PLATE 105. Tin plate mechanical rolling horse and cart. Paint on tin plate toys is rarely found as complete as is found on this horse. Excellent, $900.00; Mint, $1,800.00.

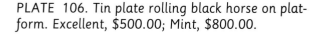

PLATE 106. Tin plate rolling black horse on platform. Excellent, $500.00; Mint, $800.00.

PLATE 107. Tin plate rolling two horse team and trolley. Rolling wheels are cast iron. Excellent, $400.00; Mint, $750.00.

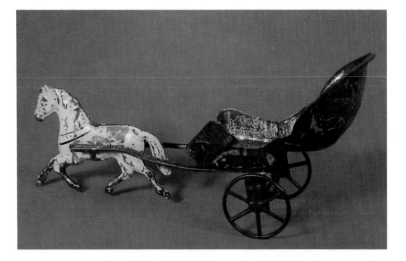

PLATE 108. Tin plate single horse pulling blue carriage.
Excellent, $500.00; Mint, $900.00.

PLATE 109. Single horse pulling wagon tin plate toy. Note the cast
iron wheels. Excellent, $350.00; Mint, $700.00.

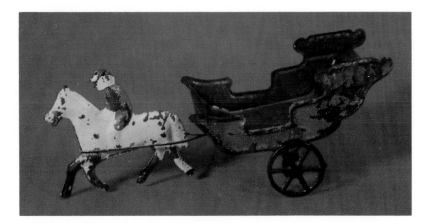

PLATE 110. Tin plate horse with rider pulling an ornate embossed
blue coach on cast iron wheels. Excellent, $400.00; Mint,
$600.00.

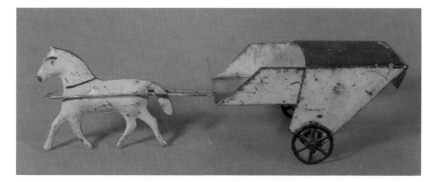

PLATE 111. Unusual yellow horse pulling yellow wagon. Note the very simple look of the wagon. Only right angles were bent to form a very stark looking wagon. Excellent, $300.00; Mint, $500.00.

PLATE 112. Dual horse team pulling wagon. Horses were painted, wagon was plated and thus has lost some of its original bright finish. Excellent, $300.00; Mint, $550.00.

PLATE 113. Cast iron "Eagle" milk man riding in wagon pulled by rolling black horse. Excellent, $700.00; Mint, $1,500.00.

PLATE 114. Cast iron Seventh Regiment Ambulance pulled by a two horse team. A rare cast iron pull toy combination. Excellent, $1,200.00; Mint, $1,800.00.

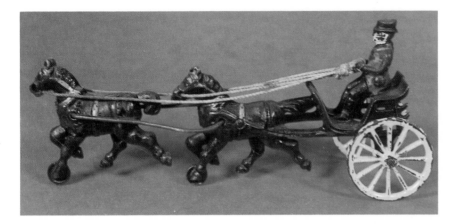

PLATE 115. Cast iron sulky wagon with bright yellow wheels pulled by two in-line horses. Cords for reins are original. Excellent, $500.00; Mint, $950.00.

PLATE 116. Cast iron and metal early automobile. Note that the steering wheel is on the right of the vehicle and it also has attached wooden headlamps. Cast iron woman passenger figure is a replacement from another toy. Circa 1890's. Excellent, $700.00; Mint, $1,200.00.

PLATE 117. Black horse pulling fancy coach and coachman. Fine details, all original paint, and completely cast iron. By Hubley. Excellent, $1,000.00; Mint, $1,700.00.

PLATE 118. Bronze finish cast iron horse and surrey. Horse has non-rolling wheel on front for balance. Excellent, $300.00; Mint, $500.00.

PLATE 119. Cast iron dual horse fire engine pumper wagon with driver, early 1900's. Excellent, $600.00; Mint, $1,200.00.

PLATE 120. Fancy cast iron fire engine drawn by two horses with driver up front and a fireman also on back. Original paint and truly a museum piece. Excellent, $800.00; Mint, $1,400.00.

PLATE 121. Cast iron pacing horse and sulky rider. Brown and bronze finish. Wheels actually roll. Excellent, $350.00; Mint, $600.00.

PLATE 122. Cast iron donkey pulling green cart. Excellent, $250.00; Mint, $450.00.

PLATE 123. Cast iron and metal elephant bell ringing pull toy. Early 20th century. Excellent, $350.00; Mint, $525.00.

PLATE 124. Cast iron coal cart, driver and horse. Horse has stationary wheel molded onto foot. Excellent, $250.00; Mint, $550.00.

PLATE 125. Cast iron horse pulling coach. Excellent, $300.00; Mint, $575.00.

PLATE 126. Cast iron horse pulling tin and cast iron milk wagon. Excellent, $350.00; Mint, $700.00.

PLATE 127. Cast iron motorcycle with sidecar and rider, with original rubber tires. Excellent, $200.00; Mint, $400.00.

PLATE 128. Cast iron early automobile with spare tire and metal wheels. Green finish with gold trim. Excellent, $800.00; Mint, $1,600.00.

PLATE 129. Red cast iron sedan with metal wheels. Excellent, $250.00; Mint, $450.00.

PLATE 130. Cast iron Auto Express 548 early pickup truck. Excellent, $800.00; Mint, $1,400.00.

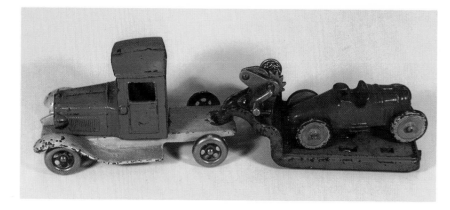

PLATE 131. Painted cast iron wrecker with flatbed trailer and working winch. Red racer is an added piece, not original to set. Excellent, $2,000.00; Mint, $3,000.00.

PLATE 132. Cast iron red racer style roadster with gold painted wheels. Excellent, $700.00; Mint, $1,400.00.

PLATE 133. Red enamel finished cast iron early sedan. Excellent, $300.00; Mint, $575.00.

PLATE 134. Yellow and black cast iron early sedan with driver. Cast iron wheels. Excellent, $500.00; Mint, $900.00.

PLATE 135. Red cast iron automobile, very early 20th century with painted metal wheels. Excellent, $700.00; Mint, $1,400.00.

PLATE 136. Cast iron early automobile with passengers. Excellent, $350.00; Mint, $600.00.

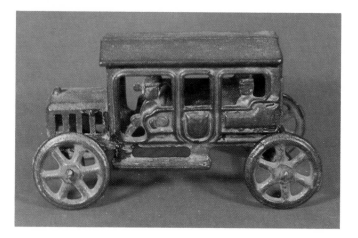

PLATE 137. Bright red cast iron fire truck with gold wheels, shown in superior condition. Excellent, $300.00; Mint, $650.00.

PLATE 138. Andy Gump comic character 348 car by Arcade with detailed Andy Gump figure driving. Excellent, $750.00; Mint, $1,400.00.

PLATE 139. Cast iron early trolley car. Excellent, $900.00; Mint, $1,700.00.

PLATE 140. Cast iron red tractor with rubber "balloon" tires. Excellent, $200.00; Mint, $450.00.

PLATE 141. Cast iron early Ford tractor with metal traction wheels. Excellent, $350.00; Mint, $650.00.

PLATE 142. Lehmann tin windup chimney sweep and the baker. Excellent, $2,700.00; Mint, $4,500.00.

PLATE 143. Tin windup Chinese dog pushing monkey in cart. Exquisite detailing. Excellent, $1,250.00; Mint, $2,000.00.

PLATE 144. Lehmann superbly detailed windup tricycle driver and woman in carriage, called the RAD-CYCLE. Excellent, $850.00; Mint, $1,800.00.

PLATE 145. Lehmann windup early automobile with driver and child, called Naughty Boy. Excellent, $900.00; Mint, $1,500.00.

PLATE 146. Colorful tin windup clown being pushed by dog. Excellent, $600.00; Mint, $1,000.00.

PLATE 147. Brightly lithographed open bed truck, EHE and Co.,by Lehmann. Excellent, $800.00; Mint, $1,500.00.

PLATE 148. Tin windup pig pulling cart with colorful lithography, bearing words "Marke Stock" Excellent, $600.00; Mint, $1,200.00.

PLATE 149. Tin lithographed donkey and clown windup toy. Excellent, $800.00; Mint, $1,250.00.

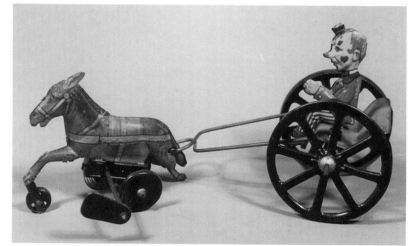

PLATE 150. "DARE DEVIL" zebra pulling cart windup toy by Lehmann. Mint, $700.00; Excellent, $1,200.00.

PLATE 151. Tin lithographed windup horseless coach, by Lehmann. Excellent, $500.00; Mint, $900.00.

PLATE 152. Lehmann tin windup toy, Germany. Excellent, $500.00; Mint, $850.00.

PLATE 153. Tin lithographed clown automobile with Punch and Judy motif around sides, complete with three characters. Excellent, $600.00; Mint, $1,250.00.

PLATE 154. OHO windup early car with driver by Lehmann. Excellent, $400.00; Mint, $850.00.

PLATE 155. Lehmann TUT TUT early windup auto showing wonderful figural detail. Excellent, $1,250.00; Mint, $2,400.00.

PLATE 156. Lehmann Onkel windup toy with very detailed figures and man holding canopy umbrella. Excellent, $550.00; Mint, $1,000.00.

PLATE 157. Tin windup woman driving three-wheeled vehicle. Excellent, $400.00; Mint, $800.00.

PLATE 158. Lehmann Zig Zag windup rolling toy with unusual action. Excellent, $1,250.00; Mint, $1,900.00.

PLATE 159. Lehmann Balky Mule tin windup toy pictured with original box. Excellent, $400.00; Mint, $725.00.

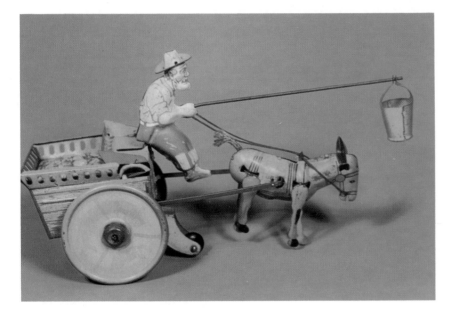

PLATE 160. Tin windup Jenny the Balking Mule, manufactured by Ferdinand Strauss. Excellent, $300.00; Mint, $550.00.

PLATE 161. RUCK-RUCK early automobile showing extremely bright and colorful lithography. Excellent, $750.00; Mint, $1,200.00.

PLATE 162. Ornately lithographed tin windup steam roller with driver. Excellent, $600.00; Mint, $1,100.00.

PLATE 163. Tin windup early lithographed tractor and plow. Excellent, $700.00; Mint, $1,200.00.

PLATE 164. Tin lithographed rolling ice wagon pulled by horse. Excellent, $400.00; Mint, $750.00.

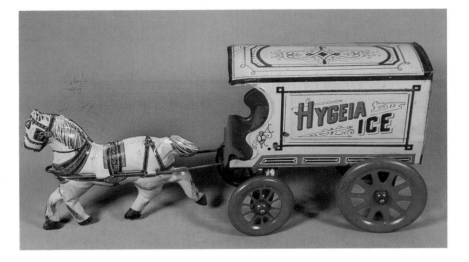

PLATE 165. Hygeia Ice tin lithographed horse drawn rolling wagon. Excellent, $600.00; Mint, $950.00.

PLATE 166. Toyland's Farm Products Milk & Cream tin lithographed horse-drawn wagon. Windup action. Excellent, $300.00; Mint, $550.00.

PLATE 167. Toyland's Farm Products Milk & Cream wagon windup, yellow and orange version with white horse. Excellent, $250.00; Mint, $500.00.

PLATE 168. Very early metal and cast iron open top roadster. Excellent, $1,250.00; Mint, $2,000.00. Bisque doll in chauffeur's costume. Excellent, $200.00; Mint, $400.00.

PLATE 169. Early Marx tin windup automobile with superior yellow paint, detailed driver, and lithographed balloon-type tires. Excellent, $900.00; Mint, $1,500.00.

PLATE 170. Tin lithographed windup early automobile with extraordinary lithographic and metallic detailing, with well-modeled driver. Excellent, $1,500.00; Mint, $2,500.00.

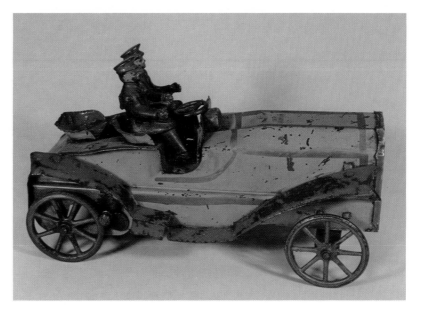

PLATE 171. Early tin and cast iron automobile with uniformed driver and passenger. Unusual painted early auto, not lithographed. Excellent, $700.00; Mint, $1,300.00.

PLATE 172. Small tin lithographed sedan with rear passengers. Excellent, $300.00; Mint, $500.00.

PLATE 173. Tin lithographed racer roadster with BENZIN marking and driver. Excellent, $600.00; Mint, $950.00.

PLATE 174. Junior oil tanker truck with bright lithography, manufactured by Strauss. Excellent, $400.00; Mint, $850.00.

PLATE 175. Dan-Dee oil truck with lithographed balloon tires manufactured by J. Chein. Excellent, $500.00; Mint, $900.00.

PLATE 176. Small tin lithographed bus with driver and upper deck. Excellent, $275.00; Mint, $450.00.

PLATE 177. Metal racer with driver and bright red wheels. Excellent, $200.00; Mint, $350.00.

PLATE 178. Inter-state Bus manufactured by Ferdinand Strauss, double decker design. Excellent, $800.00; Mint, $1,500.00.

PLATE 179. Heinz Pure Food Products delivery truck manufactured by Metal Craft. Excellent, $250.00; Mint, $500.00.

PLATE 180. Fire Chief Siren Coupe with a working siren, metal construction, manufactured by Girard. Excellent, $400.00; Mint, $650.00.

PLATE 181. International metal grocery truck by Buddy L, all metal construction. Excellent, $300.00; Mint, $650.00.

PLATE 182. Railway Express Agency delivery truck, all metal construction. Manufactured by Buddy L. Excellent, $250.00; Mint, $500.00.

PLATE 183. Sunshine Biscuits delivery truck, manufactured by Metal Craft. Excellent, $200.00; Mint, $450.00.

PLATE 184. Tin Studebaker auto in original box, manufactured by Sinsei Toys, made in Occupied Japan. Excellent, $100.00; Mint, $250.00.

PLATE 185. Hubley hook and ladder truck metal fire engine shown with original box. Excellent, $150.00; Mint, $250.00.

PLATE 186. Courtland red side loading dump truck with solid rubber wheels. Excellent, $75.00; Mint, $125.00.

PLATE 187. Tin windup motorcycle with driver and sidecar and Dunlop cord tires. Excellent, $650.00; Mint, $900.00.

PLATE 188. Policeman on motorcycle tin windup with working siren. Excellent, $400.00; Mint, $650.00.

PLATE 189. Early tin windup train with detailed lithography and head of engineer sticking out of locomotive. Locomotive, tender, and passenger coach. Excellent, $700.00; Mint, $1,250.00.

PLATE 190. Unusual tin lithographed train with stationary cloud of smoke trailing behind smokestack, all one piece. Excellent, $500.00; Mint, $900.00.

PLATE 191. Tin lithographed Southern Pacific Nonpareil Limited train with locomotive engine, tender and coach. Excellent, $600.00; Mint, $1,100.00.

PLATE 192. Tin lithographed Southern Pacific Nonpareil Limited train showing slightly different version from train in Plate 191. Excellent, $600.00; Mint, $1,100.00.

PLATE 193. Empire Express and New York Express brightly lithographed tin windup train with Chicago 515 passenger cars. Excellent, $600.00; Mint, $1,000.00.

PLATE 194. Union Pacific yellow and brown tin lithographed windup train. Excellent, $400.00; Mint, $700.00.

PLATE 195. City of New York sidewheeler steam boat, with colorful paint detailing, probably by Wilkins. Excellent, $850.00; Mint, $1,200.00.

PLATE 196. Battleship Maine wood and paper lithographed rolling boat. Probably manufactured by Bliss. Excellent, $1,200.00; Mint, $1,600.00.

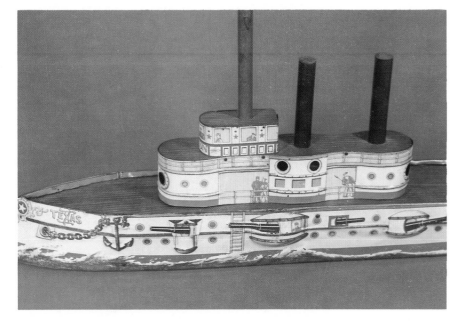

PLATE 197. Battleship Texas tin lithographed and wooden boat. Excellent, $800.00; Mint, $1,400.00.

PLATE 198. Early actual working steam powered toy boat, tin with painted detailing. Excellent, $600.00; Mint, $900.00.

PLATE 199. Four boat fleet of intricately detailed miniature steamships, early 20th century. Excellent, $800.00; Mint, $1,200.00.

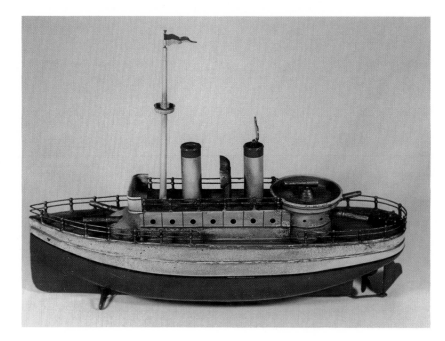

PLATE 200. Exquisitely detailed early metal steamship with working rudder and clockwork windup power. Excellent, $1,200.00; Mint, $1,900.00.

PLATE 201. U. S. Merchant Marine steamship with windup drive mechanism, and movable rudder. Manufactured by Ives. Excellent, $1,400.00; Mint, $2,000.00.

CHAPTER THREE

∾ GAMES ∾

An amazing survivor of today's forever encroaching micro-electronics and computer wizardry is the family board game. No matter how they gloss it up, put it on floppy disk, or expand it with batteries and flashing lights, the simple family board game still exists in a healthy variety. With all of the Technicolor electronics and gadgetry that we have come to expect, why hasn't the old parlor game gone by way of the dinosaurs? Good heavens! Certainly we must realize that we don't even have PARLORS anymore! Then how can we have parlor games?

The amazing answer is: family board board games have survived because the family has survived. Yes, no matter how many thousands of points we can score on our televisions with little plumbers and monsters zapping their way through mazes, there is something missing. There is no real interaction with other human beings. Now, take an afternoon filled with the likes of Monopoly, or Clue, or Risk...and a family with friends gathered around the largest table in the house. There IS the board game going on, but there is also family fellowship, conversation, laughter, anger, arguments, affection, conflict, and of course fun. What made family board games so much fun over a hundred years ago is exactly what makes them fun today. The joy comes from sharing the experience of "the game" with other human beings.

The fascination with people gathered around an interesting board game goes back well into ancient times and the earliest civilizations. However, our discussion of board games will begin with those produced in the nineteenth century and on into our present one. One of the factors that had great bearing upon the popularity and quality of board games was the development of high quality lithography. This allowed games to be mass produced with fantastic colorful designs at a relatively lost cost.

One of the other notable factors in the development of the board game was the evolution of the box design. Since board games of the Victorian era were often displayed in general stores standing up along shelving or on countertops, their container boxes and box lids grew increasingly attractive and inviting. Often, the box lid was much more exciting than the board game contained inside since it was the lid that enticed the original owner to purchase the game in the first place.

For example, the Game of Yuneek pictured in Plates 202 and 203 proves that the graphics have far greater beauty and more character than the game itself. This particular game is circa 1880's to 1890's and was manufactured by McLoughlin Brothers of New York. A box lid design that far outdoes the interior game board is the Game Of To The North Pole By Airship pictured in Plates 204 and 205. Although the game board is colorful, it in no way compares with the strong, vivid graphics of the airship crossing over the North Pole depicted on the box lid shown in Plate 204. This game was manufactured by the Milton Bradley Company of Springfield, Mass.

The District Messenger Boy game pictured in Plates 206 and 207 is another story. Both the box lid and the interior built-in game board have extremely vivid graphic designs. Notice the bright, warm color palette used for the printing of this game. Most Victorian games have this "warmth" or antique printed look that makes them so appealing to collectors. The District Messenger Boy game was also manufactured by Milton Bradley.

The Game of Bounce pictured in Plates 208 and 209 is a striking example of Victorian illustrative art found on children's board games. This exquisite game was manufactured by McLoughlin Brothers of New York in the 1890's and features an incredible banjo-playing and dancing cat on the box lid. This is rather unusual since neither the interior geometric designed game board nor the animal face spinner have anything to do with a cat. This is yet another example of how a strongly graphic game lid could draw a buyer to this game.

Spear's Comical Tivoli Game manufactured in England in the late 1890's, pictured in Plates 210 and 211, features a beautiful game box lid permanently hinged to the bottom game board. Inside the game lid is a finely detailed and functioning marble chute drop that allows a marble placed in the clown's mouth to roll back and forth down several levels until it lands in the bagatelle type game board on the bottom to score points.

The Spin It and Tiddledy Winks games pictured in Plates 214 and 215 are both from around the turn of this century and were manufactured by Milton Bradley. Toys that illustrate children at play on the cover often are more desirable to collectors than those with more generic designs. The costuming of the children on the box lids usually gives an indication of the age of the toys.

Plates 218 and 219 picture two strikingly similar toys manufactured on different continents. Plate 218 pictures the Toy-Town Telegraph Office manufactured by Parker Brothers in the very early twentieth century in America. Plate 219 pictures the similar Tiny Town Parcel Post game manufactured by Spear's Games of London, also circa early 1900's. Both contain almost identical character masks — one for a Western Union Telegraph agent and the other for a Parcel Post Carrier. The telegraph set contains a toy telegraph clicker while the parcel post set contains a standup mailing window with newspapers and "parcels" to mail.

The Happy Hooligan Game featuring a set of mint condition comic strip character targets and original cork gun pictured in Plate 226 was manufactured by Milton Bradley in the very early 1900's. Although the graphics of the lithographed standup targets inside are tremendous, they pale in comparison to the vivid comic art decorating the box lid.

The comic character games beginning in Plate 229 are proof that even early game manufacturers knew that popular characters sold more games. Therefore, we are treated to a visual potpourri of colorful game examples from Mickey Mouse and Snow White to Andy Gump and the Toonerville Trolley. Charlie Chaplin, Barney Google and Spark Plug, and Little Orphan Annie all do a tremendous job of making games stand out from the pack and be noticed. What made these games sell well originally is exactly what keeps them far more valuable today. Character recognition and visual impact help to make a good character game a GREAT ONE.

The games shared in this chapter are only a very small sampling of a tremendous wealth and variety of styles, shapes, subjects, and sizes of games available to today's game collectors. And because most families chose to store an old game in the top of a closet or attic waiting for that rainy day when they would be used again, many excellent examples of very early games are still available to today's collectors. Game collecting is certainly a recognized and respected specific area of toy collecting, but nearly everyone who loves old playthings has at least a few good old games in their collection.

Yes, chuck the hand held personal electronic game machines and those combative video blasters. Give us a wonderful old board game any day. For getting reacquainted with your family, or simply passing the hours while the snow falls outside, there's nothing better on earth than playing board games with those you love.

It's as human and homespun as life ever gets!

PLATE 202. Game of Yuneek boxed board game by McLoughlin Brothers of New York, late 1800's. Excellent, $400.00; Mint, $700.00.

PLATE 203. Game board for Game of Yuneek pictured in Plate 202.

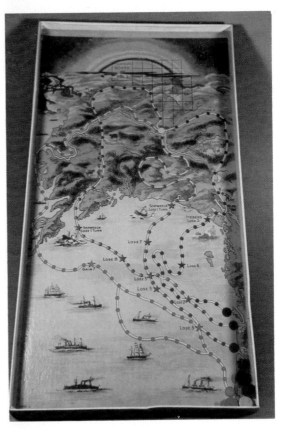

PLATE 204. Game of To The North Pole By Air-Ship, by Milton Bradley. Excellent, $250.00; Mint, $500.00.

PLATE 205. Inside playing board for North Pole game pictured in Plate 204.

PLATE 206. Game of the District Messenger Boy boxed early 20th century game by Milton Bradley of Springfield, Mass. Excellent, $200.00; Mint, $350.00.

PLATE 207. Inside playing board for District
Messenger Boy game shown in Plate 206.

PLATE 208. Game of Bounce by McLoughlin Brothers, late 1800's. Excellent,
$200.00; Mint, $450.00.

PLATE 209. Game of Bounce showing inside board
and game pieces.

PLATE 210. Spear's Comical Tivoli Game, English manufacturer. Excellent, $250.00; Mint, $400.00.

PLATE 211. Spear's Comical Tivoli Game showing inside marble drop game.

PLATE 212. Soldiers on Guard target set manufactured by McLoughlin Brothers. Excellent, $300.00; Mint, $500.00 set.

PLATE 213. McLoughlin Brothers Boys & Girls colorful lithographed alphabet cards. Excellent, $125.00; Mint, $200.00.

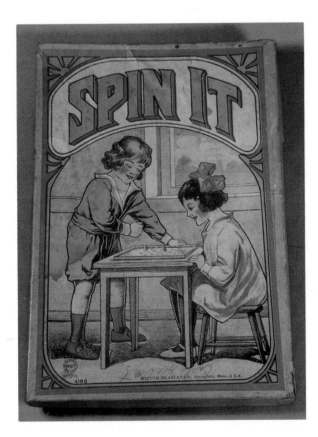

PLATE 214. Spin It top game, manufactured by Milton Bradley. Excellent, $100.00; Mint, $150.00.

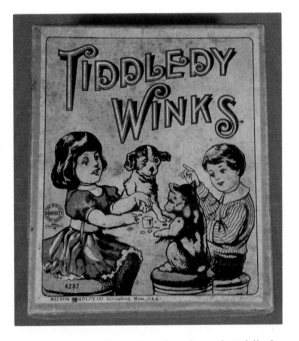

PLATE 215. Milton Bradley boxed Tiddledy Winks game, circa early 1900's. Excellent, $50.00; Mint, $100.00.

PLATE 216. Jack Straws game manufactured by Milton Bradley of Springfield, Mass. Circa early 1900's. Excellent, $50.00; Mint, $125.00.

PLATE 217. Game of Little Red Riding Hood manufactured by Clark and Snowdon of New York, early 1900's. Excellent, $75.00; Mint, $150.00.

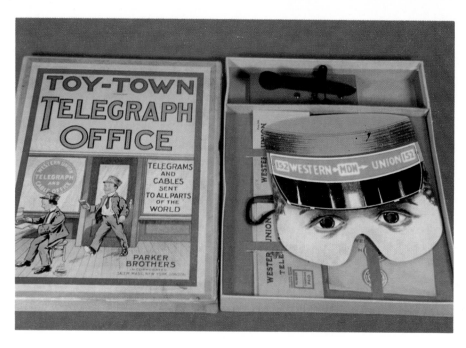

PLATE 218. Toy-Town Telegraph Office play set with lithographed and wood pieces, manufactured by Parker Brothers of Salem, Mass. Excellent, $125.00; Mint, $200.00.

PLATE 219. Tiny Town Parcel Post lithographed play set manufactured by Spear's of England. Excellent, $150.00; Mint, $250.00.

PLATE 220. We Play Store, The Game of Buy and Sell colorful lithographed cardboard game. Excellent, $50.00; Mint, $100.00.

PLATE 221. Familiar Objects, A Game For Children early picture-lotto type game set. Excellent, $100.00; Mint, $225.00.

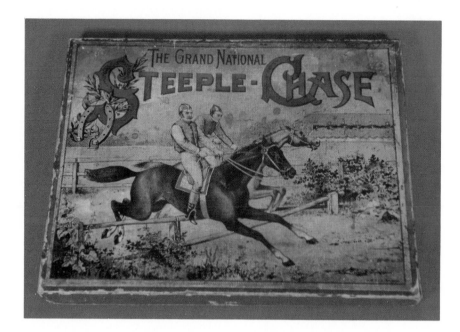

PLATE 222. Grand National Steeple-Chase game showing finely detailed lithographed lid. Excellent, $300.00; Mint, $550.00.

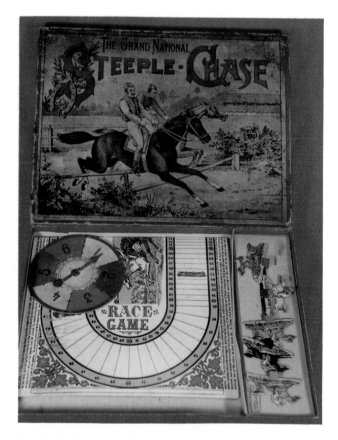

PLATE 223. Grand National Steeple-Chase game, inside playing board and original game pieces.

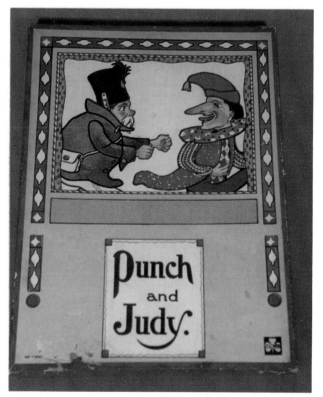

PLATE 224. Punch and Judy boxed colorfully lithographed game set. Excellent, $125.00; Mint, $275.00.

PLATE 225. Railway boxed game set showing box lid, board, and game pieces. Excellent, $75.00; Mint, $125.00.

PLATE 226. Happy Hooligan Game comic character cork gun target set, manufactured by the Milton Bradley Company. Excellent, $700.00; Mint, $1,200.00.

PLATE 227. Santa Claus Special colorful card game set in original box. Excellent, $150.00; Mint, $300.00.

PLATE 229. Andy Gump His Game lithographed boxed game set based upon the popular comic strip character. Excellent, $125.00; Mint, $200.00.

PLATE 228. Uncle Wiggily Game box for playing pieces. A matching game board accompanied this smaller game pieces box. Box & game board. Excellent, $50.00; Mint, $75.00 for box and board.

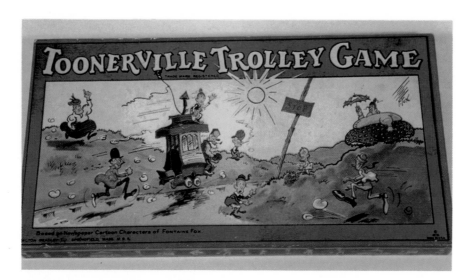

PLATE 230. Toonerville Trolley Game based upon Fontaine Fox's comic characters and manufactured by Milton Bradley. Excellent, $200.00; Mint, $400.00.

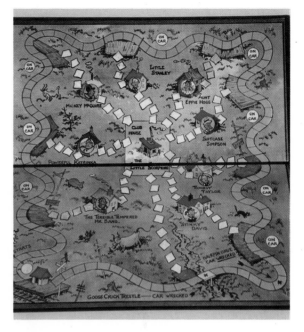

PLATE 231. Original game board for the Toonerville Trolley game pictured in Plate 230.

PLATE 232. Barney Google and Spark Plug Game, manufactured by Milton Bradley and based upon the popular Billy DeBeck comic characters. Excellent, $200.00; Mint, $450.00.

PLATE 233. Original game board for the Barney Google and Spark Plug Game.

PLATE 234. Daisy Donkey Ring Game manufactured by the Schacht Rubber Manufacturing Company complete with target and rubber rings. Excellent, $75.00; Mint, $125.00.

PLATE 235. Little Black Sambo children's book character boxed board game. Excellent, $80.00; Mint, $130.00.

PLATE 237. Mickey Mouse Bean Bag target game manufactured by the Marks Brothers company of Boston in the 1930's. Excellent, $300.00; Mint, $450.00.

PLATE 236. "Let Them All Come" ring target game featuring Mickey Mouse made by Spear's of England in the 1930's. Excellent, $400.00; Mint, $700.00.

PLATE 238. Walt Disney's own game Little Red Riding Hood boxed game set, 1934, made by Parker Brothers. Excellent, $200.00; Mint, $400.00.

PLATE 239. Mickey Mouse Tidley-winks target set manufactured by Chad Valley of England in the 1930's. Excellent, $500.00; Mint, $900.00.

PLATE 240. Walt Disney's Own Game Snow White and the Seven Dwarfs manufactured by Parker Brothers of Salem, Massachusetts in 1938. Excellent, $150.00; Mint, $300.00.

PLATE 241. Edgar Bergen's Charlie McCarthy game of Topper, circa 1930's. Excellent, $100.00; Mint, $150.00.

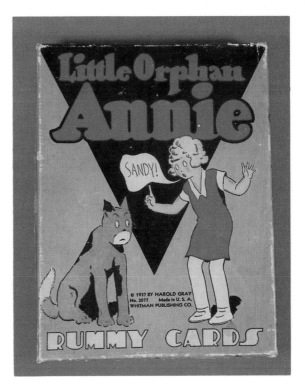

PLATE 242. Little Orphan Annie Rummy Cards manufactured by Whitman Publishing. Excellent, $75.00; Mint, $125.00.

PLATE 243. Ferdinand's Chinese Checkers with the Bee boxed game manufactured by Parker Brothers and copyright 1938 Walt Disney Enterprises. Excellent, $100.00; Mint, $200.00.

PLATE 244. Popeye Playing Card Game, copyright 1934 and published by Whitman. Excellent, $50.00; Mint, $75.00.

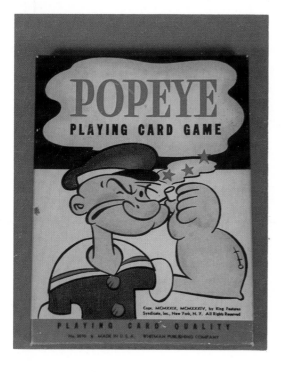

PLATE 245. Popeye Playing Card Game, manufactured by Whitman. Excellent, $50.00; Mint, $75.00.

PLATE 246. Flash Gordon boxed target games featuring beautiful box graphics. Excellent, $225.00; Mint, $400.00.

PLATE 247. Flash Gordon on the Beam vividly colorful lithographed game target, one of set in Plate 246. Target only: Excellent, $100.00; Mint, $200.00.

PLATE 248. Flash Gordon Space Target contained in set pictured in Plate 246. Target only: Excellent, $100.00; Mint, $200.00.

PLATE 249. The Red Ryder Target Game manufactured by Whitman Publishing. Excellent, $125.00; Mint, $250.00.

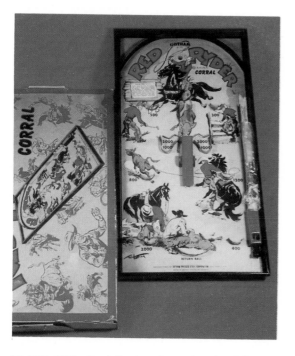

PLATE 250. Red Ryder Corral colorful target bagatelle game with original box. Excellent, $200.00; Mint, $350.00.

PLATE 251. Favorite Funnies printing set, boxed stamp set including Dick Tracy, Little Orphan Annie, Denny Dimwit, and others. Excellent, $75.00; Mint, $100.00.

CHAPTER FOUR

∾ TOYS FROM THE NURSERY ∾

This chapter covers some of those special types of toys that could be found in the children's nursery and do not necessarily fit into any of the other categories in this book. The toys contained here include doll houses, children's china and lithographed tin tea sets, early stuffed animals, a few dolls, Kewpie character items, and wooden and cast iron doll furniture.

The wonderful wood and paper lithographed doll houses dating from the late 1800's pictured in this chapter represent only a fraction of the designs that were manufactured. Most of the romantic Victorian doll houses we recognize as antique were manufactured by Bliss. Although there were other American and foreign manufacturers whose examples also show up at antique shows, it is the Bliss examples that collectors go crazy over because of the incredible detail and colorful lithography that gives these houses their special "look" of antiquity.

The doll houses pictured in Plates 252 and 253 are strong examples of this superior turn of the century lithography. Most doll houses of this type and manufacture have a front facade that can be unlatched and swings open on hinges. Nearly all doll houses found today on the collector's market are devoid of furnishings, but the Bliss Company did manufacture an incredible line of wood and paper lithographed doll house furniture. It is indeed a lucky collector who can find a Bliss doll house complete with the original furniture! The exquisite doll house pictured in Plate 255 is a classically styled Victorian beauty, complete with richly detailed period furniture.

The Raggedy Ann and Andy pictured in Plate 255 are having a fine afternoon tea. They are pictured here not only because they were and still are greatly loved childhood playthings from one of the principal contributors to this book, they also show a common arrangement of toys found in the nursery: dolls seated at a doll sized table and chairs playing with a tea set. This is a common set up found in nearly every Victorian nursery.

The Little Red Riding Hood Victorian era tin lithographed tea set pictured in Plates 256 and 257 is an example of some of the finest and richest color design found on any lithographed toys in this book. The graphics are vivid and the colors are breathtaking. Little Red Riding Hood was a popular toy theme in the very early part of the twentieth century.

All of the stuffed toy examples presented in this chapter are from the first half of the twentieth century. The teddy bear with glass eyes and jointed arms and legs shown in Plate 268 along with the rabbit with original clothes in Plate 259 and the lamb in Plate 260 are fine examples of stuffed toys. Because such toys were stored over the years, collectors should be on the lookout for signs of possible insect damage. The worst insect damage usually begins and then spreads from the area of the feet on such a toy. All of the examples pictured here are free from damage, and the stuffed and jointed monkey pictured in Plate 261 is an example of fine stuffed toy design that has survived the years. This old monkey, affectionately called "Monk" by his original owner, is a wonderful example of personality and character designed into a much loved toy.

The Kewpie characters created by Rose O'Neill were popular in the early decades of the twentieth century. O'Neill was an artist and magazine illustrator whose success and talent with these characters allowed her to branch out into book illustration while her popular characters were designed into a vast array of impressive and cute bisque doll figures, tea sets, china pieces, and ceramic figurines. The Kewpie toys pictured in this chapter begin in Plate 262.

Little girls in the nursery often loved to imitate what mother did in real life. The afternoon tea that the Victorian mother might have held was a popular event for the little Victorian girl to imitate. These little girls treated their special dolls and friends to some wonderful make believe afternoon teas on some incredible tea service. The examples pictured at the end of this chapter represent the many sets which were manufactured especially for little girls. The tin lithographed tea trays pictured in Plates 270 and 271 are clear examples that children at play was a common illustration theme. The complete boxed lithographed tin tea set pictured in Plate 274 is a mint condition example. The china tea set pictured in Plate 279 contains beautiful pink and white china with illustrations of Kate Greenaway designs in different scenes decorating every piece.

All those little nursery toys that were dearly loved by girls who had hours to spend at play with their dolls, doll houses, and afternoon teas. They represent a bygone era of innocence that can now only be brought back to life by a nostalgic visit back to restorations of the Victorian nursery.

Our great-grandmothers may no longer be with us as the years flow steadily on, but their toys from the little girls' nursery remind us of how they lived when they were young.

Anyone for a sweet cup of tea?

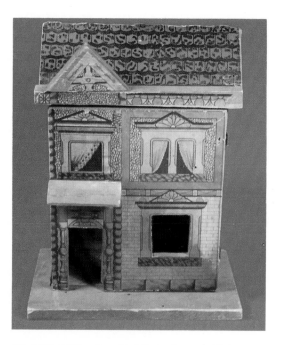

PLATE 253. Small Victorian doll house manufactured by Bliss. Excellent, $300.00; Mint, $650.00.

PLATE 252. Victorian wood and colorful lithographed paper doll house, circa early 1900's and manufactured by Bliss. Excellent, $900.00; Mint, $1,500.00.

PLATE 254. Victorian era paperboard doll house with original furniture, circa early 1900's. Excellent, $1,000.00; Mint, $2,000.00.

PLATE 255. Raggedy Ann and Andy dolls with children's furniture and china tea set. Doll Pair: Excellent, $400.00; Mint, $700.00.

PLATE 256. Tin lithographed Little Red Riding Hood storybook tea set with beautiful scenes from the story. Circa early 1900's. Excellent, $200.00; Mint, $375.00.

PLATE 257. Little Red Riding Hood and the wolf tin lithographed child's tea tray, circa early 1900's. Excellent, $100.00; Mint, $200.00.

PLATE 259. Plush rabbit with blue jacket, probably circa 1930's. Excellent, $150.00; Mint, $275.00.

PLATE 258. Early mohair jointed teddy bear with glass eyes, circa 1920. Excellent, $250.00; Mint, $475.00.

PLATE 260. Mohair lamb with glass eyes. Excellent, $125.00; Mint, $200.00.

PLATE 261. Mohair fully jointed monkey with glass eyes, circa early 1900's. With yes-no action. Manufactured by SCHUCO. Excellent, $300.00; Mint, $475.00.

PLATE 263. Rose O'Neill Kewpie character bisque reading a book in a green chair. Excellent, $500.00; Mint, $950.00.

PLATE 262. Composition Kewpie doll with purple outfit on blue base, has jointed arms. Excellent, $400.00; Mint, $800.00.

PLATE 264. Rose O'Neill Kewpies lithographed tin tea set with 4 pieces. Excellent, $250.00; Mint, $450.00 as shown.

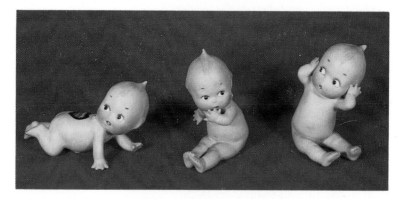

PLATE 266. Kewpie character bisque figures, set of three with original label stickers on back. Excellent, $250.00; Mint, $575.00.

PLATE 265. Dressed celluloid Rose O'Neill Kewpie figure candy container designed in a Christmas theme. Excellent, $300.00; Mint, $600.00.

PLATE 267. Pair of Rose O'Neill Kewpie character teapots. One shows them dressed as Prussian soldiers, the other pictures Chief Wag with a "K" flag in his hair. Each: Excellent, $250.00; Mint, $400.00.

PLATE 268. Kewpie Beach tin lithographed child's small sand pail picturing "Scootles" at play on the beach building a sand castle with the Kewpies. Excellent, $200.00; Mint, $375.00.

PLATE 269. Pair of jointed arm bisque dolls, circa 1920's. Excellent, $200.00; Mint, $300.00 pair.

PLATE 270. Early lithographed tin tray picturing children building an old fashioned snowman. Excellent, $75.00; Mint, $150.00.

PLATE 271. Child's tea tray picturing children playing Ring Around O'Rosie in a meadow. Circa early 1900's. Excellent, $75.00; Mint, $150.00.

PLATE 272. Child's tea tray picturing boy and girl dressed as an Indian having a picnic. Manufactured by Amsco, circa early 1900's. Excellent, $100.00; Mint, $200.00.

PLATE 273. Little Red Riding Hood tea set pieces manufactured by the Ohio Art Company of Bryan, Ohio. Excellent, $50.00; Mint, $100.00 both pieces.

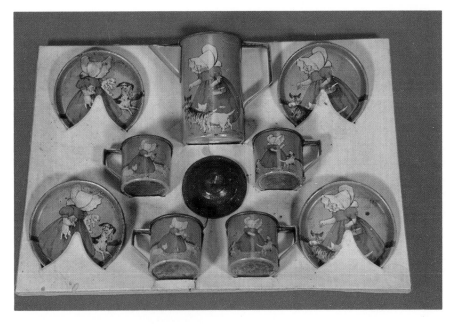

PLATE 274. Complete early child's lithographed tin tea set picturing little girl in bonnet with puppies and dog. Excellent, $300.00; Mint, $650.00 set.

PLATE 275. Early lithographed tin tea set pieces with landscape design. Excellent, $50.00; Mint, $85.00 as shown.

PLATE 276. Little Red Riding Hood child's lithographed tea set. Excellent, $125.00; Mint, $200.00 set.

PLATE 277. Mary Had a Little Lamb pair of early lithographed tin tea set pieces. Excellent, $100.00; Mint, $225.00 both pieces.

PLATE 278. Bisque baby figure with puppy and pacifier, circa early 1900's. Excellent, $150.00; Mint, $300.00.

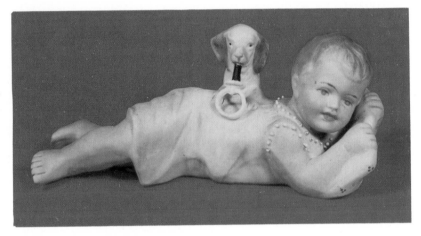

PLATE 279. Complete Kate Greenaway illustrated child's tea set, early 1900's, with beautiful detailing. Fine china. Excellent, $350.00; Mint, $600.00 set.

PLATE 280. Rose O'Neill Kewpie illustrated china baby dish. Excellent, $300.00; Mint, $550.00.

PLATE 281. Girl and dog lusterware china baby bowl. Excellent, $100.00; Mint, $150.00.

PLATE 282. Three Bears child's cup and saucer, fine china. Excellent, $75.00; Mint, $125.00.

PLATE 283. Palmer Cox Brownie characters illustrated child's china cup. Excellent, $50.00; Mint, $100.00.

PLATE 285. Uncle Wiggily and Grandpa Goosey Gander child's ceramic cup. Excellent, $40.00; Mint, $70.00.

PLATE 284. The Three Bears china child's tea set creamer. Excellent, $100.00; Mint, $150.00.

PLATE 286. Walt Disney's Bambi cream pitcher and plate manufactured in the 1940's by American Pottery. Excellent, $200.00; Mint, $350.00 both pieces.

PLATE 287. Betty Boop comic character child's lusterware tea set, 1930's Japan. Excellent, $150.00; Mint, $275.00 as shown.

PLATE 288. Buster Brown glazed ceramic plate. Excellent, $40.00; Mint, $75.00.

PLATE 289. Fancy metal toy rotary phone, circa 1930's. Excellent, $75.00; Mint, $100.00.

PLATE 290. Porcelain glazed and wooden dollhouse furniture assortment. Excellent, $50.00; Mint, $100.00 all. Excellent, $15.00; Mint, $25.00 each.

PLATE 291. Blue cast iron doll sized wood cookstove with oven, early 20th century. Excellent, $250.00; Mint, $400.00.

PLATE 292. Cast iron stove bank could have been used as a doll scale toy or actually used as a bank. See also this book's section on banks, circa 1900. Excellent, $200.00; Mint, $375.00.

PLATE 293. Small cast iron doll scale stoves. Victorian era. Each: Excellent, $150.00; Mint, $325.00.

CHAPTER FIVE

❧ WINDUP TOYS ❧

The organization of toys into this chapter is quite simple. If the toy can be wound up, and produces a resulting action, it landed in this chapter. These are wonderful reminders of yesteryear that we can still actually play with as adults! There is something incredibly captivating about a windup toy. Maybe it is the initial pleasure we derive from the tension and sound of winding up the mainspring. Maybe it is the anticipation of what is going to happen as soon as we throw the switch or move the lever to send the toy rolling, spinning, or whirling about. Or maybe it is the pleasure we get from watching the action of the toy, or maybe what is so captivating about windup toys is...they are fun! That's simple enough. They were great playthings when they were new, and they are still fun to play with.

Most windup toys from the 1920's through the 1950's were made of metal. They are often referred to as "tin windups," although not all examples were actually made out of tin. Leading manufacturers of tin windup toys in this country were the Louis Marx Company and J. Chein Toys. Both companies produced vividly colorful lithographed tin toys for many decades, and as a testimony to the durability and quality of their design, many of these toys now approaching 50 and 60 years of age are still in great working condition!

During the late 1970's and early 1980's, the interest in all windup toys skyrocketed due to the character toy phenomenon. Since comic character toy windups were continually being sold at record setting prices, general windup toys also began to show higher prices. This sent families into their attics and basements to drag out their treasure troves of tin windup toys that had not been played with in years. When the public recognizes that there is a great monetary value in old playthings, great examples of these toys start springing up.

Now that we are well into the 1990's, general toy prices seem not to be reaching such extremes. Most windup toys can be purchased in the $300 to $700 range, with rarer comic character toys or much earlier toys bringing in $1,000.00 to $2,000.00. Both dealers and collectors seem to be happy in today's market.

So, what makes up a great windup toy? First, if it has a comic character connection, its value can almost double. Second, if the toy exhibits a strikingly original design or unusual action when wound up, this increases its collectible potential. A bright, clean finish with most of the toy's original "store-bought" shine and luster never hurt to increase the value, and finally, strong lithography and graphics can help to make a windup toy a true winner.

The Ride A Rocket amusement park toy manufactured by J. Chein is an interesting windup that imitates the action of its much larger midway counterparts. When wound, the brightly colored rocket ships swing out with pleasing action as the entire canopy rotates. This toy is pictured in Plate 294. The Disneyland Ferris Wheel, also manufactured by J. Chein, is pictured in Plate 295. This colorful toy is sought after by both general windup collectors and Disneyana collectors. A generic version of the Disneyland Ferris Wheel is shown in Plate 296 with no Disney character lithography.

One of the best amusement park toy designs manufactured by Chein was their Playland Merry Go Round pictured in Plate 298. This beautiful tin windup piece has an on/off lever and windup key on the reverse. It features children riders on the removable horses and built-in swan chairs. Watching it operate is the next best thing to riding on a real carousel.

The Balloon Vendor windup pictured in Plate 301 is another famous windup toy. What makes this graphically strong toy such a hit among tin windup collectors and Disneyana collectors alike is the inclusion of a tiny Mickey Mouse doll lithographed on the small grouping of toys that hang on a string from his right hand. Although this was not a licensed Disney piece, many collectors of Disneyana consider this a Disney character windup.

The celluloid acrobatic girls windup pictured in Plate 302 is unusual because the entire design of the toy is done in celluloid, including the canopy, acrobat girl figures, and the windup base.

The Schuco windup monkeys and clown from Germany pictured in Plate 304 have felt bodies on metal frames and interesting musician windup action.

The Unique Artie crazy car driving clown is so named because he was manufactured by the Unique Art Company. This clever windup car and character are examples of the very best and brightest in metal lithography.

Many of the celluloid windup toys shown in this chapter are in superior to mint condition, which is a surprise in itself considering the fragile nature of the celluloid material. A lightweight forerunner of modern plastic, 1920's and 1930's celluloid was brittle and unforgiving. It dented, broke, and cracked quite easily. When the factor of windup action with rapid movement is added to these fragile toys, it is a wonder that any of them survived at all!

Celluloid windup toys are pictured in this chapter beginning with Plate 309 and running through Plate 332. Celluloid was a popular toy production medium because it was extremely lightweight and inexpensive to produce. The small windup mechanisms within the toys did not have to be large in order to propel or animate the very light toy designs. The windup mechanism in a celluloid windup toy is rarely obvious or distracting to the overall design since it could usually be quite tiny.

The celluloid Mary and Her Little Lamb windup pictured in Plate 314 has obvious storybook character tie-in and utilizes a main windup toy figure with the mechanism and a second cart that is drawn along behind carrying the lamb. Also interesting to note is the popular theme design of the puppy and the shoe. Three different versions of this windup toy are pictured in Plates 315 and 316.

The Henry and the Goose (Plate 318) and the Henry on the Elephant (Plate 325) are two highly desirable celluloid comic character windups. And the Mickey and Minnie Mouse acrobats (actually called Swinging Exhibition Flights) is a comic character treatment of a basic acrobatic toy design. The inclusion of the two Disney mice makes this toy an additionally hot item among Disneyana enthusiasts.

Several black minstrel toys are pictured beginning in Plate 333. These toys feature beautiful and colorful lithographed designs. The Charleston Trio (Plate 333) and Ham and Sam The Minstrel Team (Plate 334) are two much desired windups among collectors. The minstrel dancer toys pictured in Plates 335 and 336 are particularly interesting because each is shown with its original box.

The Kiddie Cyclist toy pictured in Plate 342 is one of this author's favorites. This toy manufactured by Unique Art features entertaining action when given plenty of room. The little boy "pedals" the tricycle as it rolls along; he also changes directions often and leans from side to side in an incredible imitation of reality. This toy may look great on the shelf, but it is even a bigger hit when it can be actually operated on an open floor!

The Zilotone tin windup xylophone toy pictured in Plate 353 is a most unusual toy design. The clown actually bangs or "plays" the xylophone with realistic action, and because the toy can be fitted with tune discs looking much like metal records, he can actually play the tune that a child selects. The Rodeo Joe cowboy crazy car driver pictured in Plate 360 is an extremely colorful windup design that is almost identical to that of the clown toy, Unique Artie, except for a different hat and a different lithograph design. The forms of the two toys are identical. Both Unique Artie and Rodeo Joe were manufactured by Unique Art.

The windup Monkey Cyclist pictured in Plate 362 is a fine and colorful example of the standard Louis Marx line of metal windup toys. The colorful original box is also a typical example of the pleasing Marx container box designs. The Marx Merrymakers Band tin windup mouse toy pictured in Plate 390 is often considered by collectors to be a comic character windup since the mice do bear a resemblance (abstract as it may be!) to an early art-deco Mickey Mouse. It was not a Disney licensed piece, and is actually just a generic mouse design tin windup toy by Marx.

Beginning with Plate 390 and continuing to the end of this chapter are excellent examples of comic character toy windups from the 1920's, 1930's, and 1940's. The comic character toys are the Rolls Royces of collectible tin windups. They usually command the higher prices and are often more difficult to find since mint or excellent examples are usually snapped up. The Popeye the Champ celluloid and tin windup toy pictured in Plate 391 is a splendid example of the very best in Louis Marx toy designs, shown with its very graphic original box! The lever action release windup Pinocchio Delivery cart by Louis Marx in 1939 is an interesting Disneyana windup example that is quite rare today. And the Popeye character and Charlie McCarthy windups are still quite strong among collectors of tin windups who specialize in comic characters.

Although the wild popularity of battery operated action toys which began to take hold of the toy market in the 1950's and surged into the 1960's put a damper on the unusual wealth of tin windup designs, these windups in no way became extinct. Although they will never return to the way they were in the 1920's and 1930's, new windup toys still appear on the toy market today. The fact that ANY toys are still made with windup designs in an age of micro-electronics and alkaline batteries attests to the lasting pleasure that can be derived from simply winding up a toy and letting it go.

What they gave to us in return for a couple of turns of the wrist or a twist of the fingers was nothing short of pure pleasure!

PLATE 294. Ride a Rocket tin windup amusement ride manufactured by J. Chein. Excellent, $750.00; Mint, $1,000.00.

PLATE 295. Disneyland Ferris Wheel tin lithographed windup toy manufactured by J. Chein. Excellent, $400.00; Mint, $700.00.

PLATE 296. J. Chein tin lithographed ferris wheel windup amusement park toy. Excellent, $300.00; Mint, $650.00.

PLATE 297. Tin lithographed Merry Go Round carousel windup toy with six horses. Excellent, $600.00; Mint, $900.00.

PLATE 298. Playland Merry Go Round tin windup carousel manufactured by J. Chein. Excellent, $400.00; Mint, $800.00.

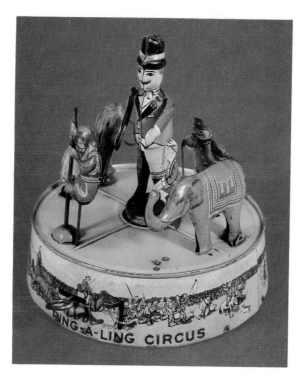

PLATE 299. Ring-A-Ling Circus windup tin lithographed circus toy with climbing monkey, lion, clown, elephant, and ringmaster. Excellent, $350.00; Mint, $550.00.

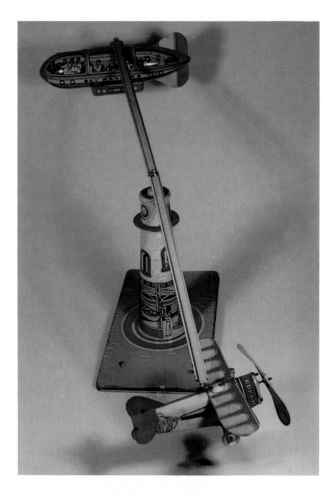

PLATE 300. Tin windup Sky Rangers blimp and airplane toy. Excellent, $400.00; Mint, $700.00.

PLATE 301. Balloon vendor tin windup toy with small Mickey Mouse dangling on a string. Excellent, $500.00; Mint, $800.00.

PLATE 302. Celluloid acrobats windup toy with multi-colored celluloid base. Excellent, $400.00; Mint, $700.00.

PLATE 303. Barnum Bailey tin windup elephant and circus wagon with line up of smaller parade animals. Excellent, $500.00; Mint, $1,000.00.

PLATE 304. Schuco monkeys and clown with mouse metal and cloth windup toys. Excellent, $250.00; Mint, $450.00 each.

PLATE 305. Tin windup flying horse carousel with added airplanes between the horses. Excellent, $300.00; Mint, $500.00.

PLATE 306. Unique Artie tin windup crazy car lithographed clown toy manufactured by the Unique Art Manufacturing Company. Excellent, $400.00; Mint, $650.00.

PLATE 307. Honeymoon Express tin windup small revolving train toy with two tunnels and one bridge. Note only the train appears on this version. By Marx. Excellent, $150.00; Mint, $275.00.

PLATE 308. Honeymoon Express tin windup plane and train action toy by Louis Marx. Note that this version has windup train AND circling plane. Excellent, $200.00; Mint, $325.00.

PLATE 309. Celluloid windup acrobat toy, circa. 1930's. Excellent, $400.00; Mint, $600.00.

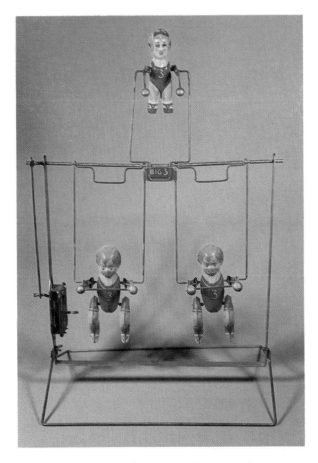

PLATE 310. Big Three windup acrobats toy manufactured by Louis Marx Company. Excellent, $450.00; Mint, $650.00.

PLATE 311. Celluloid and tin windup girl on swing and bell ringing boy. Excellent, $200.00; Mint, $400.00.

PLATE 312. Celluloid windup little clown on a donkey. Excellent, $225.00; Mint, $375.00.

PLATE 313. Celluloid windup pig pulling the clown, made in Occupied Japan. Excellent, $250.00; Mint, $350.00.

PLATE 314. Mary and Her Little Lamb celluloid windup with rolling figures on platforms. Excellent, $250.00; Mint, $400.00.

PLATE 315. Celluloid dog windup carrying metal shoe. Excellent, $250.00; Mint, $400.00.

PLATE 316. Two styles of celluloid Scotty dog windups with metal shoes. Each: Excellent, $125.00; Mint, $200.00.

PLATE 317. Little boy on scooter tin windup, Occupied Japan. Excellent, $150.00; Mint, $275.00.

PLATE 319. Kitten and butterfly celluloid windup toy. Excellent, $50.00; Mint, $125.00.

PLATE 318. Henry the comic character pulled by a goose celluloid windup toy. Excellent, $650.00; Mint, $900.00.

PLATE 320. Cowboy riding a horse celluloid windup toy. Excellent, $225.00; Mint, $275.00.

PLATE 321. Mother Bunny pushing Baby Bunny in an Easter basket celluloid windup toy. Excellent, $125.00; Mint, $225.00.

PLATE 322. Little Bear with whirling canopy celluloid windup toy. Excellent, $150.00; Mint, $250.00.

PLATE 323. Pelican in Pearls celluloid windup toy. Excellent, $75.00; Mint, $125.00.

PLATE 324. Crawling Infantryman celluloid windup toy. Excellent, $125.00; Mint, $200.00.

PLATE 325. Celluloid windup comic character Henry on the Elephant. Excellent, $1,000.00; Mint, $1,600.00.

PLATE 326. Henry on the Trapeze celluloid windup toy distributed by George Borgfeldt and pictured with original box. Excellent, $700.00; Mint, $1,000.00.

PLATE 327. Little boy with watermelon and dog celluloid windup. Excellent, $500.00; Mint, $800.00.

PLATE 328. Long-billed crawling Donald Duck celluloid windup toy copyright Walt Disney Enterprises. Excellent, $900.00; Mint, $1,500.00.

PLATE 329. Celluloid windup horse pulling The Covered Wagon. Excellent, $250.00; Mint, $400.00.

PLATE 330. Celluloid windup baseball catcher toy, Occupied Japan. Excellent, $275.00; Mint, $425.00.

PLATE 331. Celluloid windup Mexican riding a donkey extremely colorful action toy. Excellent, $350.00; Mint, $600.00.

PLATE 332. Mickey and Minnie Mouse Swinging Exhibition Flights windup celluloid action figures, 1930's, George Borgfeldt Distributors. Excellent, $900.00; Mint, $1,250.00.

PLATE 333. Charleston Trio black minstrels and dog roof top dancers windup by Louis Marx. Excellent, $1,200.00; Mint, $1,500.00.

PLATE 334. Ham and Sam The Minstrel Team tin windup action toy with colorful tin lithography. Manufactured by the Ferdinand Strauss Company. Excellent, $900.00; Mint, $1,400.00.

PLATE 335. Jazzbo Jim The Dancer on the Roof tin windup toy featuring minstrel dancer with banjo and original box. Manufactured by Louis Marx. Excellent, $650.00; Mint, $900.00.

PLATE 336. Tombo minstrel tin windup dancer manufactured by Ferdinand Strauss. Shown with original box. Excellent, $700.00; Mint, $1,100.00.

PLATE 337. Sunny Andy Fun Fair multiple action windup lithographe tin toy. Excellent, $150.00; Mint, $275.00.

PLATE 338. Sunny Andy Kiddie Kampers metal windup multiple figure action toy. Excellent, $200.00; Mint, $350.00.

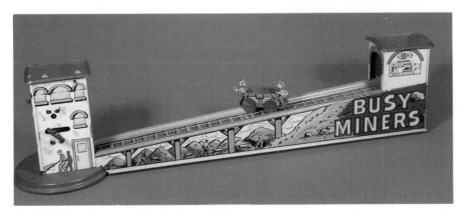

PLATE 339. Busy Miners coal car and track tin windup toy by Louis Marx. Excellent, $150.00; Mint, $275.00.

PLATE 340. Busy Bridge finely detailed tin windup cars on bridge toy manufactured by Louis Marx. Excellent, $400.00; Mint, $625.00.

PLATE 341. Panama Pile Driver lithographed tin windup action toy. Excellent, $200.00; Mint, $350.00.

PLATE 342. Unique Art Company brightly lithographed tin windup Kiddie Cyclist action toy. Excellent, $375.00; Mint, $500.00.

PLATE 343. Louis Marx Company's tin windup Yellow Cab car. Excellent, $125.00; Mint, $200.00.

PLATE 344. Tin lithographed number nine race car with man and woman. Excellent, $175.00; Mint, $250.00.

PLATE 345. Old Jalopy tin windup junk car manufactured by Louis Marx. Excellent, $175.00; Mint, $250.00.

PLATE 346. "Baby Tractor" tiny tin lithographed windup tractor. Excellent, $100.00; Mint, $200.00.

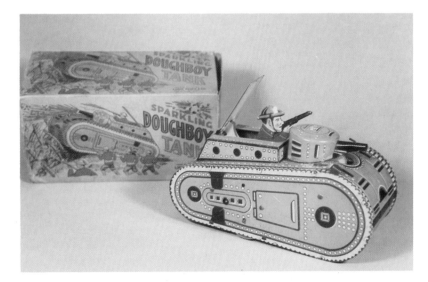

PLATE 347. Sparkling Doughboy Tank manufactured by Louis Marx Company, featured up and down action of doughboy with rifle inside. Original box shown. Excellent, $200.00; Mint, $350.00.

PLATE 348. Marx tin windup Tank Corps U. S. Army No. 3 windup toy. Excellent, $125.00; Mint, $200.00.

PLATE 349. Lithographed tin windup hand car. Excellent, $125.00; Mint, $200.00.

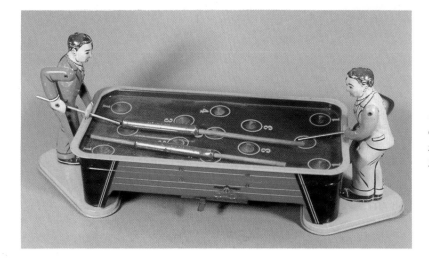

PLATE 350. Billiards players tin lithographed windup toy with player cue sticks. Excellent, $200.00; Mint, $400.00.

PLATE 351. Play Golf windup golfer manufactured by the Ferdinand Strauss Corp. of New York. Excellent, $375.00; Mint, $525.00.

PLATE 352. Tin windup handcar manufactured by Girard featuring action of two riders. Excellent, $150.00; Mint, $225.00.

PLATE 353. Zilotone tin windup musical clown toy. Excellent, $250.00; Mint, $450.00.

PLATE 354. Tin windup ice cream man on cart with bell. Excellent, $200.00; Mint, $350.00.

PLATE 355. Balky Mule toy manufactured by Louis Marx. Excellent, $100.00; Mint, $175.00.

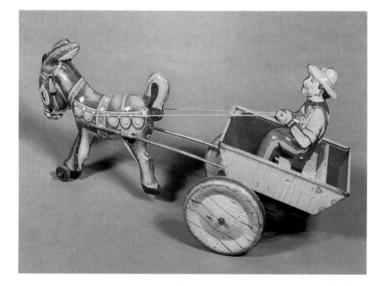

PLATE 356. Flash Gordon Rocket Fighter tin lithographed windup action toy. Excellent, $350.00; Mint, $600.00.

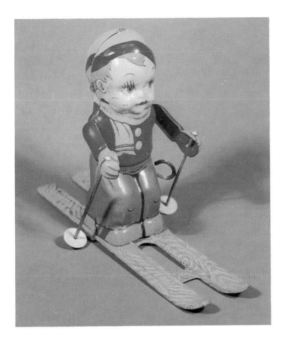

PLATE 357. J. Chein Company tin windup boy on skis. Brightly colorful lithography. Excellent, $150.00; Mint, $250.00.

PLATE 358. Girard windup metal grinder toy. Excellent, $125.00; Mint, $175.00.

PLATE 359. Milton Berle Crazy Car manufactured by Marx. Excellent, $400.00; Mint, $750.00.

PLATE 360. Rodeo Joe tin windup crazy car manufactured by Unique Art. Excellent, $300.00; Mint, $450.00.

PLATE 361. Cowboy windup crazy car featuring colorful cowboy driver with cow face wheels. Manufactured by Louis Marx. Excellent, $700.00; Mint, $1,000.00.

PLATE 362. Monkey Cyclist tin windup monkey on tricycle manufactured by Louis Marx. Shown with original box. Excellent, $275.00; Mint, $375.00.

PLATE 363. Jumbo The Walking Elephant tin windup toy. Excellent, $150.00; Mint, $250.00.

PLATE 364. Selection of three windup maids. Left is Betty, center is a maid with swinging arms and metal broom, and right is Mammy. All three are "walkers" that move about randomly and were manufactured by Lindstrom. Each: Excellent, $175.00; Mint, $275.00.

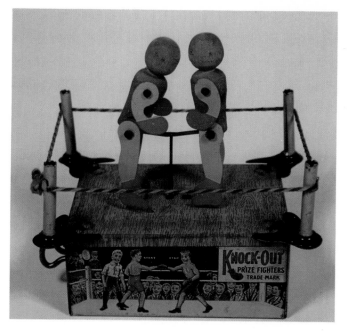

PLATE 365. Knock-out Prize Fighters tin and wooden windup toy by Ferdinand Strauss. Excellent, $500.00; Mint, $675.00.

PLATE 366. German crank windup train toy in penny toy sized scale. Excellent, $200.00; Mint, $300.00.

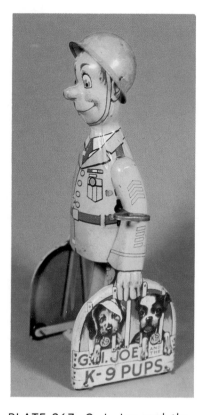

PLATE 367. G. I. Joe and the K-9 Pups windup toy manufactured by Unique Art. Excellent, $225.00; Mint, $350.00.

PLATE 368. Unique Art G. I. Joe in the Jet Propelled Jeep, tin windup. Excellent, $200.00; Mint, $400.00.

PLATE 369. Musical butterflies windup toy, tin and silk. Excellent, $125.00; Mint, $225.00.

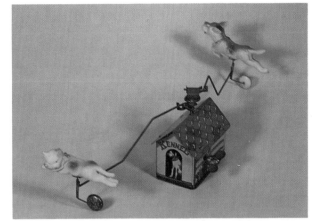

PLATE 370. Dog chasing cat celluloid and tin windup toy. Excellent, $250.00; Mint, $375.00.

PLATE 371. Porter and baggage tin lithographed windup toy. Excellent, $150.00; Mint, $250.00.

PLATE 372. Balancing clown windup acrobat toy manufactured by J. Chein. Excellent, $100.00; Mint, $200.00.

PLATE 373. Tin windup tropical child riding a giant turtle. Excellent, $200.00; Mint, $375.00.

PLATE 374. Cowboy with spinning lariat riding a dapple horse, tin lithographed windup toy manufactured by Louis Marx. Excellent, $225.00; Mint, $350.00.

PLATE 375. Circus monkey riding a cycle brightly colored tin windup toy. Excellent, $150.00; Mint, $250.00.

PLATE 376. Seal balancing a spinning ball cloth and metal windup. Excellent, $150.00; Mint, $200.00.

PLATE 377. Long-billed duck lithographed tin waddler toy by J. Chein. This toy is often mistaken for a Donald Duck windup, but Chein did not license a windup Donald. Excellent, $75.00; Mint, $125.00.

PLATE 378. Little dog tin windup with great action as all four legs scurry to move him along. Excellent, $75.00; Mint, $125.00.

PLATE 380. Mr. Sputnik, The Satellite Man metal windup toy. Excellent, $125.00; Mint, $225.00. Plush windup action dog. Excellent, $100.00; Mint, $200.00.

PLATE 380. Tin lithographed windup pecking bird. Excellent, $75.00; Mint, $125.00.

PLATE 381. Planter's Peanut advertising windup "Mr. Peanut" features early all plastic construction. Excellent, $200.00; Mint, $450.00.

PLATE 382. Tin windup porter carrying two bags, lithographed toy. Excellent, $300.00; Mint, $475.00.

PLATE 383. Tin lithographed windup drummer on platform base. Excellent, $200.00; Mint, $400.00.

PLATE 384. Tin windup drummer boy with very colorful design manufactured by Marx. Excellent, $200.00; Mint, $300.00.

PLATE 385. Rollover Plane tin windup toy manufactured by Louis Marx and shown with original box. Excellent, $325.00; Mint, $450.00.

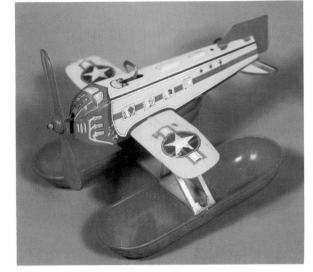

PLATE 386. Tin windup sea plane with two landing floats manufactured by J. Chein. Excellent, $250.00; Mint, $400.00.

PLATE 387. Pepsi-Cola plastic windup vendor toy shown with original box. Excellent, $150.00; Mint, $300.00.

PLATE 388. Tin windup artillery gun and soldier. Gun features spring load action. Excellent, $150.00; Mint, $275.00.

PLATE 389. Little Pig tin windup toy manufactured by J. Chein. Excellent, $75.00; Mint, $150.00.

PLATE 390. Marx Merry Makers Band, art deco styled, 1930's tin windup toy manufactured by the Louis Marx Company. Excellent, $850.00; Mint, $1,300.00.

PLATE 391. Popeye The Champ celluloid and tin windup toy manufactured by Louis Marx and shown with original box. Excellent, $1,800.00; Mint, $2,500.00.

PLATE 392. Pinocchio Delivery toy windup manufactured by Louis Marx and copyright Walt Disney Productions, 1939. Excellent, $600.00; Mint, $1,000.00.

PLATE 393. Little Orphan Annie and her dog Sandy tin lithographed windup pair. Manufactured by Louis Marx in the 1930's. Pair: Excellent, $750.00; Mint, $1,200.00.

PLATE 394. The Powerful Katrinka tin windup toy. As toy moves along, Katrinka also lifts the boy and the wheelbarrow. Excellent, $1,300.00; Mint, $2,000.00.

PLATE 395. Happy Hooligan windup tin mechanical toy manufactured by J. Chein. Excellent, $475.00; Mint, $750.00.

PLATE 396. Walt Disney's Dumbo tin windup jumping and flipping toy manufactured by Louis Marx. Excellent, $400.00; Mint, $550.00.

PLATE 397. Wood composition character windup Joe Carioca, the Disney parrot. Excellent, $450.00; Mint, $600.00.

PLATE 398. Felix The Cat riding a scooter windup toy. Felix is missing an arm. Copyright Pat Sullivan 1920's, manufactured by Nifty. Excellent, $1,100.00; Mint, $1,600.00.

PLATE 399. Maggie and Jiggs tin character windup toy. Excellent, $1,600.00; Mint, $2,000.00.

PLATE 400. Left: Joe Penner and his duck Goo-Goo tin windup. Excellent, $600.00; Mint, $900.00. Right: Harold Lloyd tin windup walker toy. Excellent, $650.00; Mint, $1,000.00.

PLATE 401. Amos 'n Andy tin lithographed windup walker toys. Pair: Excellent, $1,300.00; Mint, $2,000.00.

149

PLATE 402. Popeye The Pilot tin windup comic character airplane, manufactured by Marx. Excellent, $700.00; Mint, $1,100.00.

PLATE 403. Popeye and Olive Oyl roof dancers tin windup toy manufactured by Louis Marx. Excellent, $900.00; Mint, $1,500.00.

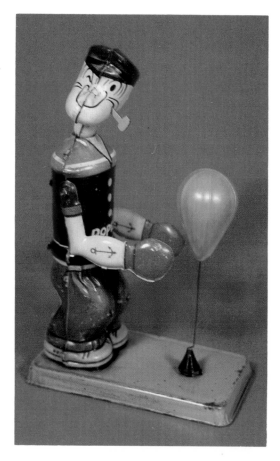

PLATE 404. Popeye with the punching bag tin windup character toy by J. Chein. Excellent, $900.00; Mint, $1,300.00.

PLATE 405. Barnacle Bill Popeye look-alike toys manufactured by J. Chein. Left is Barnacle Bill in a barrel, right is Barnacle Bill walker toy. Each: Excellent, $475.00; Mint, $725.00.

PLATE 406. Left: Popeye Express tin character windup by Marx with Popeye pushing parrot and suitcase. Excellent, $700.00; Mint, $1,000.00. Right: Popeye with parrot cages tin windup by Marx. Excellent, $500.00; Mint, $800.00.

PLATE 407. Moon Mullins and Kayo character windup manufactured by Louis Marx and shown with original box. Excellent, $700.00; Mint, $1,100.00.

PLATE 408. Charlie McCarthy and Mortimer Snerd "We'll Mow You Down" colorful windup limo, ©1939. Heads swivel as car speeds along. Excellent, $1,200.00; Mint, $1,700.00.

PLATE 409. Charlie McCarthy Benzine Buggy tin windup crazy car, circa 1930's. Excellent, $900.00; Mint, $1,200.00.

PLATE 410. Rear: B. O. Plenty tin windup Dick Tracy character walker. Excellent, $250.00; Mint, $475.00. Front: Dick Tracy Squad Car tin windup by Marx. Excellent, $250.00; Mint, $400.00.

PLATE 411. Left: Charlie McCarthy tin windup walker toy with movable mouth. Excellent, $600.00; Mint, $900.00. Right: Mortimer Snerd windup walker companion piece to Charlie McCarthy. Excellent, $650.00; Mint, $800.00.

PLATE 412. Left: Porky Pig cowboy with lariat windup by Marx. Excellent, $275.00; Mint, $450.00. Right: Porky Pig with umbrella tin windup by Marx. Excellent, $275.00; Mint, $450.00.

PLATE 413. Dagwood's Solo Flight tin lithographed character windup manufactured by Marx. Excellent, $750.00; Mint, $1,000.00.

PLATE 414. Uncle Wiggily colorful crazy car children's storybook character tin windup by Marx. Excellent, $500.00; Mint, $800.00.

CHAPTER SIX

∽ CHARACTER TOYS ∽

Since Richard Outcault first created his Yellow Kid comic strip for William Randolph Hearst's newspapers around the turn of the century, the American public has gone crazy over the popular characters presented in the funny papers. Little did Outcault, who also created Buster Brown and his dog Tige, realize that he had started a character toy phenomenon that continues to this day. The popularity of character toys for nearly an entire century now has been staggering. The intensity of this popular culture phenomenon is enough to make a collector wonder how toy designers ever got along in the days before there were comic, radio, movie, or television characters to reproduce and market into toys.

Beginning with the Yellow Kid toys pictured in Plates 415 through 417 it is clear to see how far back our fascination with comic characters goes. Outcault's Yellow Kid was highly unusual in the fact that he did not speak by the use of cartoonist's "balloons" that emanated from the characters mouths. What the Yellow Kid had to say was printed right on the front of his long, smocked shirt in casual print!

Fontaine Fox and his "Toonerville Trolley" comic strip followed in the very early part of the twentieth century as did comic strip characters by other creative cartoonists who penned the likes of "The Katzenjammer Kids" (see Plate 418 for an unusual cast iron toy based on this comic strip), "Mutt and Jeff" (see Plate 421 for two interesting dolls of these characters) and Happy Hooligan (see Plate 422). Fontaine Fox's Toonerville Trolley inspired one of the simplest, yet most clever toy designs ever. Fox's Toonerville Trolley windup trolley car pictured in Plate 419 features wonderful wobbly windup action as the car moves around a circular track. It appears when working that it is just about to rattle apart!

Another early comic character toy prized by collectors is the Barney Google riding Spark Plug windup toy pictured in Plate 420. This toy features both funny action as Barney rides his horse and superior color lithography with a brilliant finish. This toy represents all that is best in early comic character toy design.

The Charlie Chaplin windup toy pictured in Plate 415 represents a departure from comic strip influenced character toys. As Hollywood movies became increasingly popular, toys patterned after film stars and movie characters began to increase in abundance. Thus, newspaper comic characters and Hollywood movie characters began to compete for the attentions of the toy buying public.

The Skippy toys pictured in Plates 427 through 430 represent an early character that appeared in two mediums. Skippy was a highly popular comic strip character penned by Percy Crosby, and also an extremely popular national radio show character. Thus, character toy collectors are treated to Skippy comic strip and radio show collectibles.

Pat Sullivan's famous cat, Felix, was an extremely popular comic/cartoon character in the 1920's and 1930's. Because of his black and white monochrome palette, what Felix the Cat toys lack in color, they make up for in wonderful design. The two different Felix the Cat composition dolls pictured in Plates 437 and 438 are particularly striking designs of this most graphic cat. The Felix dated 1922 pictured in Plate 440 has remarkable fully jointed, solid wood construction.

Popeye the Sailor also ranks high as a long lasting popular comic strip character. Toys featuring Popeye, Olive Oyl, Wimpy, Sweet Pea, and the gang usually boast wonderful full color graphics and great action designs. The Popeye and Sweet Pea Xylophone pull toy pictured in Plate 447 is a particularly fine example of color and action combined. The Popeye Chase rolling toys pictured in Plates 449 and 450 are also fine examples of full color action graphics. These toys represent fine quality lithography on paper labels applied to wooden toys.

Harold Gray's comic strip "Little Orphan Annie" brought to life the spirit of a tough, optimistic little girl and her mongrel dog who would never give up, even in the face of tremendous adversity.

Because of this, Little Orphan Annie was a sort of patriotic child-hero to little girls everywhere. Consequently, her likeness found its way into a wonderful array of products designed for little girls of the 1930's. One of the finest Little Orphan Annie toys pictured in this chapter is the composition Annie doll in Plate 454. The doll's design is wonderfully accurate to her comic strip counterpart, and the graphics on the box that she was originally packaged in are incredible! This is one of the rare cases in collecting where the original container is probably worth far more than the toy itself! The Little Orphan Annie china tea set pictured in Plate 453 is also worthy of special note because of its exquisite and fine detail reproduced clearly and colorfully onto the surface of the china. Additionally, the three metal Little Orphan Annie stoves pictured in Plates 456 through 458 are particularly interesting for comparison of their designs.

Walt Disney comic strip and cartoon classic characters Mickey Mouse and Donald Duck have long been considered the "Cadillac" characters of toy collecting. This may be due to the fact that when the great renaissance of character toy collecting began in the sixties thanks to the likes of Andy Warhol with his "pop art" and other popular art influences, it became the "in" thing to own an old Mickey Mouse watch or have a poster of Donald Duck. The Disney characters led the way to making it completely sane and fashionable for mature adults to still hold an attachment for the cartoon characters they loved so dearly as children. As a result, since the mid-1960's, Disneyana collecting has taken charge of the character toys marketplace and led the way.

Some of the most recognizable and valuable of the 1930's Disney character toys are the different versions of windup train handcars manufactured by the Lionel Corporation. The introduction of Disney character toys to the Lionel production line in the mid-1930's helped put that corporation in the black ink and save it from bankruptcy. After saving Lionel, Mickey Mouse became a bona fide business hero! The mouse mania merchandising bandwagon was already rolling and the character toy phenomenon, led by Mickey and Donald, was here to stay!

Disneyana collectors today are much more knowledgeable than their 1960's counterparts. Today's Disney character toy collector has a wealth of information at his disposal since several ongoing and updated price guide series have been devoted to this specific field. Because of this vast available knowledge and resource material, the Disneyana collectors of the 90's are quite selective in regard to condition and rarity of toys, and significantly informed about the value of most Disneyana examples. Consequently, major bargains in the field of Disneyana collecting are few and far between.

Some of the most reasonable buys in Disneyana collecting today are the variety of tin lithographed beach and tea toys manufactured by Ohio Art in the 1930's. Several examples of sand pails by this company are pictured in this chapter. Because these toys were built sturdily with the intention for them to be played with on the beach and in the sandbox, many near mint condition examples of these vivid beach toys exist today (see Plates 482 and 489).

Disney characters from the feature films also inspired some wonderful toys, from the Three Little Pigs and Ferdinand the Bull to Snow White and Pinocchio.

A selected sampling of other character toys has also been included in this chapter, although each piece presented is just the tip of another specialty area of collecting. Flash Gordon and all of the magic of the early space toys, cowboy and western hero character collectibles, Howdy Doody representing early television characters, and Warner Brothers Looney Tunes characters have all been selected to whet the appetite of character collectors. The early Warner Brothers character collectibles of the 1940's are particularly interesting with the likes of Bugs Bunny, Daffy Duck, Elmer Fudd, and Porky Pig. These character collectibles are the ones to watch in the 1990's because of the increased interest in second generation Looney Tune characters (otherwise known as "Tiny Toons") and the building emphasis that Warner Brothers Pictures is placing on family entertainment. As the popularity of this major studio with its new-found interest in family movie fare increases, so will the interest in the golden age characters created by this studio. Mickey Mouse is the king of the cartoon world, but Bugs and his pals are deserving of far more attention than they have been getting. They're the ones to watch in the collectibles marketplace.

With every new comic strip, children's movie, or television show served up to today's children, the field of potential character collectible merchandise increases. The more characters created; the more "stuff" in the marketplace. The collectibles that will have the hottest values in ten or twenty or even fifty years will be those that are hard to find, were in short supply when they were new, and are linked with still popular and recognizable characters. It is a little hard to predict popular culture trends and habits a half a century in advance, but it would be a safe bet to assume that character toy collecting will still be alive and well.

As long as Americans are still around to have any kind of fun, they will love the character merchandise inspired by the comic and cartoon characters they loved as children. The love of these toys will last.

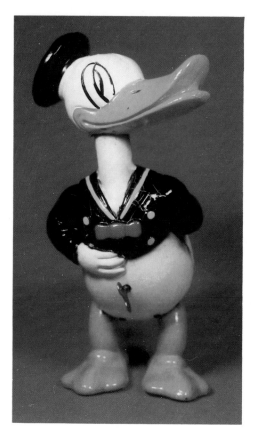

PLATE 416. Yellow Kid composition doll, circa early 1900's. Excellent, $800.00; Mint, $1,100.00.

PLATE 415. Yellow Kid cast iron, metal and fabric figure on wood block. Very early 1900's. Excellent, $600.00; Mint, $900.00.

PLATE 417. Left: Yellow Kid metal posing doll with replaced yellow robe, early 1900's. Excellent, $600.00; Mint, $900.00. Right: Yellow Kid doll, metal, print robe, early 1900's. Excellent, $700.00; Mint, $1,000.00.

PLATE 418. Katzenjammer Kids painted cast iron pull toy, early 1900's, with mechanical action. Excellent, $2,000.00; Mint, $2,700.00.

PLATE 420. Barney Google on Spark Plug the horse tin character windup toy based on characters created by Bill DeBeck. Excellent, $1,200.00; Mint, $1,700.00.

PLATE 419. Toonerville Trolley tin windup trolley car marked "copyrighted by Fontaine Fox" features wobbly windup running motion. Excellent, $700.00; Mint, $1,000.00.

PLATE 421. Mutt and Jeff composition and metal framework character dolls can be posed nicely because of their interesting jointed structure. Pair: Excellent, $1,000.00; Mint, $1,600.00.

PLATE 422. Happy Hooligan chalk type composition figure, possibly a carnival piece. Excellent, $250.00; Mint, $400.00.

PLATE 423. Barney Google and Spark Plug, copyright King Features Syndicate and manufactured by Schoenhut. Both dolls feature jointed limbs, with Barney Google being composition, and Spark Plug solid wood. Pair Excellent, $1,500.00; Mint, $2,000.00.

PLATE 424. Foxy Grandpa bisque toothpick holder character figure, circa early 1900's. Excellent, $350.00; Mint, $600.00.

PLATE 425. Charlie Chaplin tin and cast iron windup toy with excellent lithographed likeness of "The Little Tramp." Excellent, $950.00; Mint, $1,600.00.

PLATE 426. Left: Charlie Chaplin chalk type figure. Excellent, $125.00; Mint, $200.00 Center: Mutt cartoon character chalk figure. Excellent, $100.00; Mint, $175.00 Right: Jeff cartoon character chalk figure. Excellent, $100.00; Mint, $175.00.

PLATE 427. Skippy Paint and Coloring Set, based upon the Percy Crosby character and manufactured by American Toy Works. Excellent, $150.00; Mint, $275.00.

PLATE 429. Skippy character ceramic cereal bowl advertising Wheaties cereal. Excellent, $75.00; Mint, $125.00.

PLATE 428. Interior view of the Skippy Paint and Coloring Set.

PLATE 430. Skippy cellu-loid jointed character doll or crib toy. Excellent, $200.00; Mint, $350.00.

PLATE 431. Charlie McCarthy character radio manu-factured in the 1930's by Majestic. Painted cast metal figure of Charlie McCarthy is attached to the front of the radio case. Excellent, $1,100.00; Mint, $1,700.00.

PLATE 432. Left: Brightly painted Charlie McCarthy chalkware figure, circa 1930's. Excellent, $100.00; Mint, $200.00. Right: Charlie McCarthy wood composition bank with pull-string movable mouth, 1930's. Excellent, $250.00; Mint, $375.00.

PLATE 433. Reg'lar Fellers comic strip characters microscope set in original character decorated storage box. Excellent, $125.00; Mint, $250.00.

PLATE 434. Moon Mullins and Kayo ceramic lusterware ashtray, 1930's. Paint detailing on this example is exquisite. Excellent, $125.00; Mint, $200.00.

PLATE 435. Speedy Felix wooden roadster pull toy with wooden, rolling wheels, 1930's. Excellent, $650.00; Mint, $1,000.00

PLATE 436. Felix in the Airplane candy container, features a paper composition Felix in a wooden bi-plane. Excellent, $350.00; Mint, $600.00.

PLATE 437. Large Felix the Cat composition doll with jointed arms and original label on his chest. Copyright Pat Sullivan. Excellent, $675.00; Mint, $1,100.00.

PLATE 438. Large Felix the Cat composition figure with his arms folded behind his back. Copyright Pat Sullivan. Excellent, $600.00; Mint, $1,000.00.

PLATE 439. Small tin doll carriage with colorful lithography featuring a tiny scene of a girl with Felix on the side. Excellent, $375.00; Mint, $600.00. In the doll buggy is a tiny Felix the Cat solid celluloid toy. Excellent, $125.00; Mint, $200.00.

PLATE 440. Felix the Cat all wooden jointed doll, circa 1920's. Excellent, $275.00; Mint, $500.00.

PLATE 441. Betty Boop and her dog Bimbo ceramic lusterware ashtray, circa 1930's. Excellent, $150.00; Mint, $225.00.

PLATE 442. Betty Boop wooden ukulele featuring colorful design of Betty Boop, Ko Ko, and Bimbo on the front. Excellent, $250.00; Mint, $375.00.

PLATE 443. Skeezix and Uncle Walt ceramic bisque toothbrush holder, 1930's. Excellent, $150.00; Mint, $250.00.

PLATE 444. Skeezix's dog Pal boxed napkin holder. Excellent, $100.00; Mint, $200.00.

PLATE 445. Popeye Cheers Christmas lights in box, copyright 1929 King Features Syndicate. Excellent, $150.00; Mint, $250.00.

PLATE 446. Popeye Alarm Clock with lithographed graphics on the outside case, copyright King Features Syndicate. Excellent, $500.00; Mint, $1,000.00.

PLATE 447. Popeye and Sweet Pea pull toy featuring excellent paper lithographed character designs, manufactured by Metal Masters. Excellent, $250.00; Mint, $425.00.

PLATE 448. Rubber Popeye characters manufactured by Remple, 1930's. Left: Popeye. Center: Olive Oyl. Right: Wimpy. All figures are hollow rubber with squeakers in the bottom. Each: Excellent, $75.00; Mint, $125.00.

PLATE 449. Bluto and Olive Oyl Popeye characters pull toy. Paper lithographed label on wood with wooden wheels. Excellent, $250.00; Mint, $400.00.

PLATE 450. Popeye and Sweet Pea pull toy with paper lithographed label and wooden wheels. Excellent, $250.00; Mint, $400.00.

PLATE 451. Little Lulu Soap and Toiletries set, circa 1930's, in its original box. Excellent, $150.00; Mint, $225.00.

PLATE 452. Harold Teen wooden ukulele with colorful applied character decals. Excellent, $350.00; Mint, $475.00.

PLATE 453. Little Orphan Annie glazed ceramic child's tea set dishes with colorful Orphan Annie design. Excellent, $150.00; Mint, $275.00.

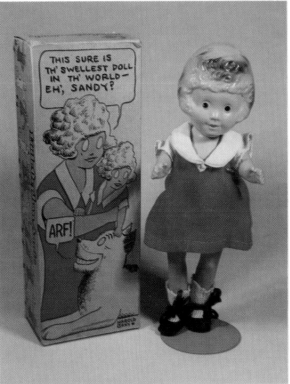

PLATE 454. Little Orphan Annie wood composition character doll in original clothes and shown with its original box, circa 1930's. Copyright by Harold Gray. Excellent, $600.00; Mint, $950.00.

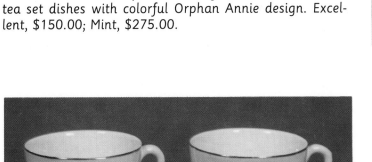

PLATE 455. Orphan Annie and Sandy pulling a wishbone pair of ceramic tea cups, circa 1930's. Pair: Excellent, $50.00; Mint, $100.00.

PLATE 456. Little Orphan Annie metal toy stove with colorful Annie and Sandy lithographed metal picture plate. Excellent, $50.00; Mint, $100.00.

PLATE 457. Little Orphan Annie metal stove, 1930's, with 4 lithographed name plates. This particular model is electric and actually heats up when plugged in. Copyright Harold Gray. Excellent, $75.00; Mint, $125.00.

PLATE 458. Little Orphan Annie stove, 1930's, with unusual upper deck baking oven. All metal construction with electric warmer built in. Excellent, $125.00; Mint, $175.00.

PLATE 459. Henry comic character large jointed doll, with two movable arms. Circa 1930's. Excellent, $250.00; Mint, $375.00.

PLATE 461. Buttercup comic character windup toy. Composition construction with fabric clothes. Excellent, $400.00; Mint, $650.00.

PLATE 460. Amos and Andy chalk ashtray, circa 1930's. Excellent, $150.00; Mint, $225.00.

PLATE 462. Buttercup and Spare Ribs tin lithographed pull toy with character graphics around base of toy. Excellent, $775.00; Mint, $1,000.00.

PLATE 463. Scrappy comic character pull toy. Paper lithographed labels on solid wood. Toy features xylophone playing action which really makes music as toy is pulled along. Excellent, $250.00; Mint, $375.00.

PLATE 464. Scrappy Christmas Tree Set with plastic comic character lamp covers, manufactured with Mazda lamps and shown with fold-up display card inside. Excellent, $150.00; Mint, $225.00.

PLATE 465. Mickey and Minnie Mouse handcar by Lionel, 1930's and copyright Walt Disney Enterprises. Pictured with original box. Excellent, $900.00; Mint, $1,400.00.

PLATE 466. Donald Duck and Pluto Rail Car manufactured by the Lionel Corporation of New York and copyright Walt Disney Enterprises. Excellent, $900.00; Mint, $1,400.00.

PLATE 467. Mickey Mouse celluloid windup nodder toy, 1930's. Mickey's head nods up and down when rod in base is wound. Excellent, $850.00; Mint, $1,300.00.

PLATE 468. Mickey Mouse composition and wood doll manufactured by Knickerbocker in the 1930's. This is referred to as the Mickey doll with "lollipop" hands. Excellent, $650.00; Mint, $900.00.

PLATE 469. Ceramic Mickey Mouse glazed pitcher, 1930's Japan. Excellent, $100.00; Mint, $150.00.

PLATE 470. Mickey Mouse Cowboy doll manufactured by Knickerbocker in the 1930's. Shown with original gun, chaps, and cowboy hat. Excellent, $1,000.00; Mint, $2,000.00.

PLATE 471. Mickey and Minnie Mouse French cookie tin with excellent character graphics on lid and around sides. From the 1930's. Excellent, $275.00; Mint, $400.00.

PLATE 472. Mickey Mouse and Pluto action pull toy from the 1930's. Copyright Walt Disney Enterprises. Excellent, $600.00; Mint, $975.00.

PLATE 473. Mickey Mouse Mechanical Racing Car from the 1930's shown with its original box. Copyright Walt Disney Enterprises. Excellent, $425.00; Mint, $600.00.

PLATE 474. Mickey Mouse Christmas Lights by Noma with bright decals on plastic lamp covers. From the 1930's. Copyright Walt Disney Enterprises. Excellent, $200.00; Mint, $275.00.

175

PLATE 475. Mickey Mouse jointed wood composition doll with movable arms, manufactured by Knickerbocker in the 1930's. Excellent, $600.00; Mint, $850.00.

PLATE 476. Long-billed Donald Duck composition doll with jointed legs and movable head. Manufactured by Knickerbocker in the 1930's. Copyright Walt Disney Enterprises. Excellent, $875.00; Mint, $1,400.00.

PLATE 477. Long-billed Donald Duck composition calendar holder figure from 1937. Holds unused calendar hanging from metal rod in his hands. This is an unusual factory adaptation by Lionel which used the Donald character figure from their Donald and Pluto hand car. Excellent, $200.00; Mint, $325.00.

PLATE 478. Mickey Mouse Drummer pull toy, by Fisher Price, copyright Walt Disney Enterprises. From the mid-1930's. When pulled, Mickey plays the cymbals and beats the drum. Excellent, $475.00; Mint, $600.00.

PLATE 479. Mickey Mouse heavy paper and cardboard pencil case, 1930's, by Dixon. Copyright Walt Disney. Excellent, $275.00; Mint, $450.00.

PLATE 480. Mickey Mouse celluloid windup toy from the 1930's, made in Japan. As toy rolls on metal base and wheels, celluloid canopy above whirls. Excellent, $975.00; Mint, $1,500.00.

PLATE 481. Mickey Mouse chalk composition lamp made by Soreng-Mangold Company in the 1930's. Excellent, $1,200.00; Mint, $2,000.00.

PLATE 482. Left: Mickey Mouse Ohio Art tin sand pail picturing Mickey and Minnie riding in a canal boat. Excellent, $275.00; Mint, $500.00. Right: Mickey Mouse washer with original wringer, 1930's. Manufactured by Ohio Art. Excellent, $450.00; Mint, $575.00.

PLATE 483. Beautiful tin Mickey Mouse flashlight from the 1930's by USA Light with scene of Mickey, Minnie and Pluto running in the woods at night. Excellent, $300.00; Mint, $475.00.

PLATE 484A. Mickey Mouse night light from the 1930's by Micro-Lite, copyright Walt Disney Enterprises. Excellent, $175.00; Mint, $300.00.

PLATE 484B. Mickey Mouse Bagatelle boxed game set manufactured by Chad Valley of England in the 1930's. Excellent, $450.00; Mint, $550.00.

PLATE 484C. Mickey Mouse Giant Bagatelle manufactured by Chad Valley in the 1930's. Made in England. Excellent, $400.00; Mint, $600.00.

PLATE 484D. Mickey Mouse Printing Outfit, manufactured by P. R. S. Co. Ltd. of London in the 1930's. Excellent, $150.00; Mint, $250.00.

PLATE 484E. Mickey and Minnie Mouse tin lithographed child's tea tray (8" long) manufactured in France in the 1930's. Excellent, $200.00; Mint, $300.00.

PLATE 485. Mickey Mouse Hankies shown with the original colorful lithographed paper box, copyright Walt Disney Enterprises, 1930's. Excellent, $200.00; Mint, $375.00.

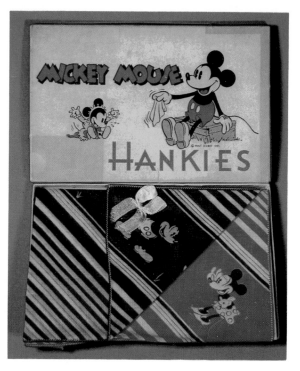

PLATE 486. Mickey Mouse Jig-Saw Puzzle from the 1930's in its original box. Manufactured by Chad Valley of England. Excellent, $200.00; Mint, $300.00.

PLATE 487. Left: Minnie Mouse bisque figure,1930's, 5" tall. Excellent, $250.00; Mint, $425.00. Center: Long-billed Donald Duck figure with two jointed arms, 1930's, 6" tall. Excellent, $750.00; Mint, $1,000.00. Right: Mickey Mouse bisque figure, 1930's, 5" tall. Excellent, $250.00; Mint, $425.00.

PLATE 488. Mickey Mouse pencil case from the 1930's manufactured by Dixon, USA. Excellent, $200.00; Mint, $325.00.

PLATE 489. Left: Small Mickey Mouse tin sand pail, 1930's, by Ohio Art. Excellent, $200.00; Mint, $275.00. Center: Giant Mickey sand pail by Ohio Art. Excellent, $375.00; Mint, $600.00. Right: Mickey Mouse 1930's Ohio Art sand pail. Excellent, $275.00; Mint, $400.00.

PLATE 490. Mickey Mouse cup and saucer set, 1930's, glazed ceramic. Made in England. Excellent, $125.00; Mint, $175.00.

PLATE 491. Mickey Mouse and Pluto ceramic cup and plate by Patriot China in the 1930's. Copyright Walt Disney Enterprises. Excellent, $200.00; Mint, $300.00.

PLATE 492A. Mickey Mouse "Fireman Mickey" ceramic cup and plate set by Patriot China of the Salem China Company, 1930's. Excellent, $200.00; Mint, $300.00.

PLATE 492B. Donald Duck china tea service picturing a very long-billed Donald figure on all pieces. Manufactured in England during the 1930's set. Excellent, $200.00; Mint, $300.00 set.

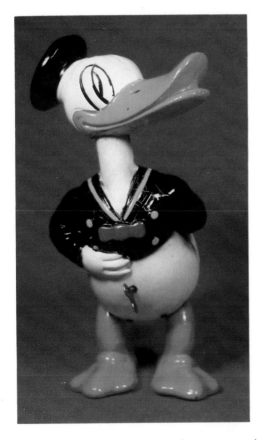

PLATE 493. Donald Duck 12" wood composition windup doll by Knicker-bocker, 1930's. Excellent, $1,300.00; Mint, $2,000.00.

PLATE 494. Mickey Mouse child's wooden hat stand, 1930's. Excellent, $275.00; Mint, $375.00.

PLATE 495. Left: Donald Duck 1930's celluloid windup toy, made in Japan. Excellent, $1,200.00; Mint, $1,700.00. Right: Long-billed Donald Duck rubber squeak toy, 1930's, manufactured by Seiberling Latex Products. Excellent, $200.00; Mint, $300.00.

PLATE 496. Donald Duck back up wooden windup toy by Fisher Price showing angry Long-billed Donald. Excellent, $1,800.00; Mint, $3,000.00.

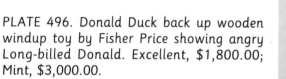

PLATE 497. Snow White Dwarfs pull toy picturing Bashful, Sneezy, and Doc. Manufactured in Europe in the 1930's. Excellent, $300.00; Mint, $450.00.

PLATE 498. Snow White, Mickey Mouse, and Disney characters Belgian tin, 1930's. Lithography on most Belgian tins is colorful and superior. Excellent, $450.00; Mint, $600.00.

PLATE 499. Snow White and the Seven Dwarfs large lithographed tin container, from Belgium, 1930's. Excellent, $300.00; Mint, $475.00.

PLATE 500. Snow White and the Seven Dwarfs Belgian tin, 1930's. Excellent, $300.00; Mint, $475.00.

185

PLATE 501. Ferdinand the Bull wooden pull toy from the 1930's, copyright Walt Disney Enterprises. Excellent, $200.00; Mint, $325.00.

PLATE 502. Ferdinand the Bull jointed wood composition doll by Ideal Toy and Novelty Company, copyright Walt Disney Enterprises, 1938. Excellent, $200.00; Mint, $425.00.

PLATE 503. Dopey the Disney Dwarf pull toy by Fisher Price, copyright 1938 Walt Disney Enterprises. Excellent, $250.00; Mint, $375.00.

PLATE 504. Snow White wood composition radio by Emerson, © Walt Disney Enterprises, 1938. Excellent, $1,200.00; Mint, $1,700.00.

PLATE 505. Left: Pinocchio jointed wood and composition doll by Ideal Toy and Novelty, 1939. Excellent, $350.00; Mint, $500.00. Right: Jiminy Cricket wood jointed character doll by Ideal Toy and Novelty, 1939. Excellent, $275.00; Mint, $400.00.

PLATE 506. Left: Happy dwarf 1938 Disney doll by Richard Krueger of New York. Excellent, $275.00; $400.00. Center: Snow White doll by Ideal Toy and Novelty, 1938. Excellent, $250.00; Mint, $425.00. Right: Sneezy dwarf doll by Richard Krueger of New York, 1938, Walt Disney Enterprises. Excellent, $275.00; Mint, $400.00.

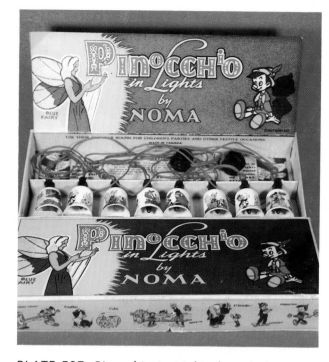

PLATE 507. Pinocchio in Lights boxed character lights by Noma, copyright 1939. Excellent, $300.00; Mint, $425.00.

PLATE 508. Pinocchio composition character bank showing Pinocchio riding on the back of a turtle, copyright 1939 by Walt Disney Enterprises and manufactured by Crown Toy and Novelty. Excellent, $275.00; Mint, $425.00.

PLATE 509. Pinocchio Ring the Nose game, copyright Walt Disney Productions, 1939. Excellent, $75.00; Mint, $125.00.

PLATE 510. Walt Disney's Pinocchio Express pull toy, circa 1939 and manufactured by Fisher Price Toys. Excellent, $300.00; Mint, $475.00.

PLATE 511. Flash Gordon Space Outfit vest, belt, and original box manufactured by Esquire Novelty Company. Excellent, $250.00; Mint, $425.00.

PLATE 512. Flash Gordon boxed set of three puzzles manufactured by Milton Bradley and copyright King Features Syndicate. Excellent, $75.00; Mint, $150.00.

189

PLATE 513. Moon Mullins and Kayo bisque toothbrush holder, 1930's. Excellent, $150.00; Mint, $225.00.

PLATE 514. Dick Tracy Target copyright by Chester Gould and licensed by Famous Artist Syndicate. Excellent, $100.00; Mint, $175.00.

PLATE 515. Dick Tracy Machine Gun, hard plastic, with Dick Tracy decal on the side. Excellent, $75.00; Mint, $140.00.

PLATE 516. Dick Tracy Siren Pistol, all metal, produces siren effect when trigger is pulled. Excellent, $100.00; Mint, $150.00.

PLATE 517. Sparkle Plenty Dick Tracy character Christmas Tree Lights, featuring 15 character lamps. Circa 1950's Excellent, $175.00; Mint, $250.00.

PLATE 518. Red Ryder Gun and Holster boxed set manufactured by Daisy Manufacturing Company of Plymouth, Michigan. Excellent, $175.00; Mint, $300.00.

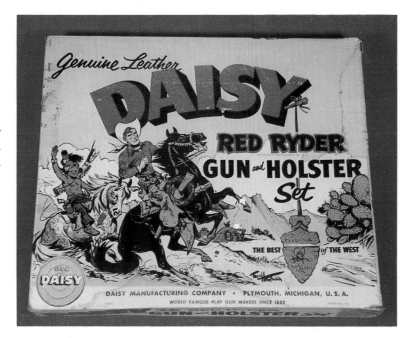

PLATE 519. Hopalong Cassidy character lunchbox manufactured by Aladdin Industries of Nashville, TN. Excellent, $100.00; Mint, $150.00.

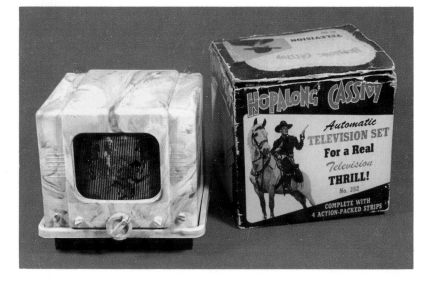

PLATE 520. Hopalong Cassidy Automatic Television Set, 1950's, featuring a "moving" picture on the windup screen. Shown with original box. Excellent, $75.00; Mint, $150.00.

PLATE 521. Lone Ranger large carnival chalk figure, shown with original paint. Excellent, $75.00; Mint, $125.00.

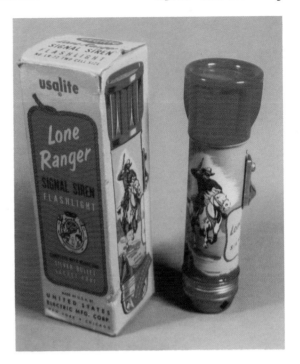

PLATE 522. Lone Ranger Signal Siren Flashlight manufactured by USA Lite. Excellent, $150.00; Mint, $225.00.

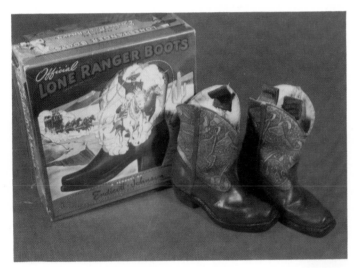

PLATE 523. Official Lone Ranger Boots manufactured by Endicott-Johnson and shown with original box. Excellent, $100.00; Mint, $150.00.

PLATE 524. Lone Ranger and His Great Horse Silver, hard plastic construction, shown with original box. Excellent, $125.00; Mint, $200.00.

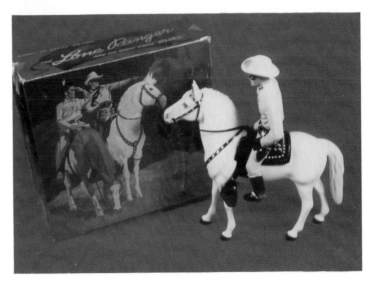

PLATE 525. Left: J. Fred Muggs television character pull toy, 1950's based upon NBC Today show chimp. Excellent, $150.00; Mint, $240.00. Right: J. Fred Muggs rubber figure, 1950's. Excellent, $75.00; Mint, $110.00.

PLATE 526. Howdy Doody Clock-A-Doodle windup toy and play clock. Original very graphic box and bright tin lithographed toy. Excellent, $900.00; Mint, $1,600.00.

PLATE 527. Left: Howdy Doody plastic Ovaltine premium mug, 1950's. Excellent, $25.00; Mint, $50.00 Right: Howdy Doody push puppet toy by Kohner Products, 1950's. Excellent, $125.00; Mint, $200.00.

PLATE 528. Howdy Doody Sand Forms manufactured by Ideal toy, 1950's. Toys are shown
on their original display card. Excellent,
$100.00; Mint, $140.00.

PLATE 529. Howdy Doody Phono Doodle
toy record player with colorful Howdy
character decorations, 1950's. Excellent,
$100.00; Mint, $225.00.

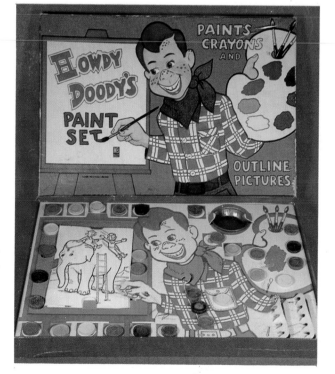

PLATE 530. Howdy Doody's Paint, Crayons,
and Outline Pictures drawing and paint set,
1950's. Excellent, $150.00; Mint, $200.00.

PLATE 532. Howdy Doody ceramic child's breakfast plate, 1950's. Excellent, $60.00; Mint, $100.00.

PLATE 531. Howdy Doody large composition and cloth body puppet with pull-string opening mouth and original costume. Circa 1958. Excellent, $275.00; Mint, $425.00.

PLATE 533. Bugs Bunny doll dressed as Davy Crockett with coonskin cap, from the 1950's. Excellent, $175.00; Mint, $325.00.

PLATE 534. Bugs Bunny on a tricycle pull toy featuring bright paper lithographed label on wood. Excellent, $225.00; Mint, $350.00.

PLATE 535. Elmer Fudd Fire Chief Car #7 bell ringing pull toy. Wood construction with wooden wheels and colorful paper lithographed label. Excellent, $175.00; Mint, $300.00.

PLATE 536. Bugs Bunny storyland record and storybook set, a "Capitol Record Reader Set" by Capitol Records and copyright Warner Brothers. Excellent, $35.00; Mint, $60.00.

PLATE 537. Left: Sniffles the Mouse, mouse and washtub planter, pot metal, by Moss Company. Copyright Warner Brothers. Excellent, $125.00; Mint, $175.00. Right: Sniffles the Mouse, mouse and tree stump planter, pot metal, by Moss Company, copyright Warner Brothers. Excellent, $125.00; Mint, $175.00.

PLATE 538. Porky the Bandmaster ceramic cup, marked "©.L.S." for Leon Schlesinger. Circa 1940's. Excellent, $50.00; Mint, $75.00.

PLATE 539. Left: Bugs Bunny glazed ceramic figure by Evan K. Shaw, 1940's. Excellent, $150.00; Mint, $225.00. Center: Daffy Duck glazed ceramic figure by Evan K. Shaw, 1940's. Excellent, $200.00; Mint, $325.00. Right: Porky Pig glazed ceramic figure by Evan K. Shaw, 1940's. Excellent, $100.00; Mint, $200.00.

PLATE 540. Left: Sniffles the Mouse glazed ceramic planter, 1940's, Evan K. Shaw. Excellent, $150.00; Mint, $200.00. Center: Standing Sniffles figure, Evan K. Shaw. Excellent, $125.00; Mint, $175.00. Right: Seated Sniffles, Evan K. Shaw. Excellent, $125.00; Mint, $175.00.

CHAPTER SEVEN

∽ PENNY TOYS, BANKS, AND METAL TOYS ∼

This chapter introduces two specialized areas of toy collecting and one very general one. The first two sections of this chapter deal with penny toys and banks, followed by a section picturing general line metal toys. All three of these areas could be considered a specialty area of collecting by some collectors, although penny toy and bank collecting are by far the most specialized areas.

The several examples of penny toys pictured in Plates 541 through 548 show the intricate detail and beauty found in these toys. Called penny toys because of their relative inexpense when they were new, most examples now command well into the hundreds of dollars. A recent increased interest in these tiny tin lithographed toys has helped to shorten the available supply on the collector's marketplace and drive prices up. Twenty years ago, penny toys could be purchased easily in the under $25 price range because of their small size and relative unimportance among many general toy collectors. With the popularity of all aspects of toy collecting that exploded in the 1980's, the popularity of these compact, high quality toys skyrocketed and today rarer examples of these toys (such as the trolley car pictured in Plate 547) can bring in excess of $500 when the right dealer links up with the serious collector.

Why, then, have they become so popular? One theory is that after an interest in these miniscule play-things was finally kindled, supplies began to dry up. Because these toys are so tiny, they were often lost, thrown out, or discarded as worthless novelties. Granted, on the surface, their small size does make them appear to be less valuable and significant than a tin windup, but it is the scarcity of mint condition pieces that appeals to today's collectors.

Another positive aspect of collecting penny toys is that their small size makes them the ideal collectible for toy lovers who are cramped for space. A sampling of six or so colorful penny toys looks tremendous in one of the tiny brass and glass miniature showcases available at import stores for well under $20. A collector can house an incredible penny toy collection in less space than is taken up by the average typewriter or desktop computer. In an age where compactness is often a practical asset, penny toys are about the most compact and impressive small collectible that exists.

Another interesting characteristic of penny toys is their design and intricate detail. Most of the penny toys actually DO something. They roll, spin, twirl, or have moving parts that may swing or bob up and down. The early automobile penny toys pictured in Plate 543 and the horse and carriages pictured in Plate 544 are wonderful examples of penny toys designed to roll. Because of their lightweight construction, most of these examples roll quite nicely. The unusual baby in the highchair penny toy pictured in Plate 542 presents the interesting action of a rolling table convertible to a highchair. When the toy is pivoted on its middle joint, the rolling table or car flips up to convert to a stationary baby in the highchair toy.

The elephant and cart penny toy pictured in Plate 546B is an excellent example of a bobbing head action toy. Aside from the little cart actually rolling behind the elephant, at the slightest motion, the elephant's head bobs up and down and side to side. This is achieved through the simplest of designs. An almost microscopic metal hook fits through a tiny hole in the elephant's neck to produce this almost frictionless movement. Take note. When this toy is found in complete mint condition, buy it. The tiny hook and hole construction is so fragile (and the head is quite easily, completely removed) that perfect examples of this toy must be quite few and far between.

The mother and baby in the buggy and the sewing machine with turning crank (pictured in Plate 548) are fine examples of the incredible detailing of the lithography on penny toys. They may have been cheap to purchase originally, but they are not at all cheap in design. Today, penny toys are a highly legitimate and popular specialized area of antique toy collecting.

Bank collecting is another respected area of toy collecting. Quite often, toy collectors specialize in only this one area of collecting. One of the reasons for this specialization is that collectors can find plenty of banks to collect even if that is their only area of specialization.

Banks are most often classified into three major areas in regard to their actions. The most common banks are referred to as "still banks" or "figural still banks." These banks were usually manufactured in cast iron and consist of two molded halves (usually a front and a back) joined together by a single screw in the back. Still banks are called such because their figures do not move; that is, they have no moving parts or actions that they can perform. These are simply stationary molded figures. These are also the most common types of banks found, although some unusual still bank versions can be quite rare.

A second classification of toy banks is those that are called "semi-mechanical." This type of bank usually consists of a very SIMPLE action. A clown may stick out his tongue and pull a coin back in. An elephant may take a coin placed on its trunk and flip or roll it back inside the slot. Most "semi-mechanical" banks consist of a single figure performing one very simple action to get the coin into the slot.

Finally, the grandfather of all toy banks among collectors is the mechanical bank. Usually, it is the fine old mechanical banks that bring the staggering prices at toy auctions. Rare mechanical banks in near mint condition can bring thousands and thousands of dollars! Mechanical banks usually consist of a pair of figures performing a sequence of actions to get the coin shot, thrown, kicked, passed, catapulted, handed, or slid into the open slot. Some versions, such as the speaking dog mechanical bank pictured in Plate 550 require not only the action of one character to initiate, but also a second action such as the dog's mouth opening to receive the coin. This combination of actions and more sophisticated design is what makes true mechanical banks so desirable. It is also the fact that these additional moving parts make such banks even harder to find in working, collectible quality order.

One of the most frustrating aspects of cast iron still bank collecting today is the difficulty new collectors may have in spotting reproductions. Rusty, chipping paint on an apparently old cast iron bank is not a definite indication of age. It is amazing how reproduction banks that are less than a year old can be made to appear old. It doesn't take much effort to age a repro, so there are literally thousands of new banks out in the collector's marketplace to snag the novice collector.

The best advice here is to KNOW THE SUBJECT MATTER before plunking down your hard earned cash. Read as many books as possible on the subject of banks, both still and mechanical. Study all illustrations carefully to get a good "feel" for the true age indications of an actual vintage cast iron bank. (The age of the screw holding the bank together is usually one good clue since the metal screws of today can't be aged as quickly as the cast iron main body of the banks.) Also, suspicious looking too-bright paint is usually a dead giveaway of a repainted example or a reproduction. There is a certain "look" and patina on old castiron banks that just cannot be reproduced, no matter how good the painter. Learning to recognize original paint finishes can be one of the easiest and clearest ways to identify genuine old banks. Many of the still figural banks pictured in this chapter were molded into the likenesses of animals, a very popular theme for late nineteenth century and early twentieth century banks. Since these were actually fashioned to be used by youngsters for saving money, they are usually quite sturdy and have most pleasing designs. The removable screw holding most two-half constructed examples of cast iron still banks gave children easy access to their coins.

Later examples in this chapter picture still banks constructed of tin with bright lithography or wood composition with lacquer and paint finishes. Most of these later examples have metal trap doors in the bottom or base of the bank that could be opened with a key. The metal trap doors are often found intact; the original keys for these examples are much harder to find.

The Warner Brothers Looney Tune character banks featuring the likes of Bugs Bunny, Elmer Fudd, and Porky Pig pictured in Plates 583 and 584 are rather common but highly collectible banks today. Because of their pleasing design and attractive paint finishes and colors, this unique line of cast metal character banks manufactured by Moss is highly collectible.

The cast iron still bank Saint Bernard pictured in Plate 553, the Boxer dog still bank pictured in Plate 554, and the Camel pictured in Plate 567 are particularly fine examples of the intricate detailing in the mold design on many of the early cast iron banks.

Moving from penny toys and banks, the chapter concludes with an array of toys classified simply by their construction as metal toys. Two of the most unusual and fine designs pictured in this section are the two different versions of a similar action mechanical train car. The Hobo Train pictured in Plate 587 was manufactured by Unique Art. The Travelchiks Train Car with its different theme but similar design was manufactured by the Ferdinand Strauss Company of New York.

The sandbox and beach toys combined with the children's action tops pictured at the conclusion of this chapter are interesting examples of more common metal toys. Also shown are miscellaneous toys from the early twentieth century which are given as a sample of the more common, everyday toys that were played with by children in the first half of this century. This includes several rubber and composition figural toys, seasonal Easter Bunny type metal lithographed push and pull toys, and a unique selection of actual firing target sets from the 1940's and 1950's.

From the penny toys and their intricate detail and beauty, the solid strength of design and uniqueness of action of the cast iron banks, and the everyday warmth and fun durability of the metal beach toys and target sets, this chapter has introduced a broad spectrum of toys covering nearly 50 years.

Whether it was the caring hands of a little child that boxed them away finally for safekeeping or a knowing adult who preserved these treasures for a generation or two speculating that one day, they would again be very important, the toys pictured here are a testimony to the fact that good things last. For one reason or another, every toy pictured in this chapter was saved by someone.

Like good friends and toy collectors alike, these old memories of childhood are in good company. They have survived.

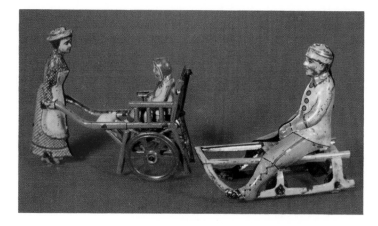

PLATE 541. Penny toys: Left: Woman and child in carriage, about 2" tall. Lithographed tin with rolling wheels. Excellent, $125.00; Mint, $200.00. Approx. 2" tall Right: Boy on sled tin lithographed rolling penny toy. Approx. 2" long. Excellent, $150.00; Mint, $225.00.

PLATE 542. Left: Baby in convertible high chair tin lithographed penny toy with wheels, approx. 2" tall. Excellent, $160.00; Mint, $220.00. Right: Baby carriage tin lithographed penny toy with little girl holding ball and doll. Excellent, $175.00; Mint, $240.00.

PLATE 543. Left: Penny toy auto, tin lithographed toy with rolling wheels, approx. 2" long. Excellent, $200.00; Mint, $325.00. Right: Blue tin lithographed touring car with rolling wheels penny toy. Approx. 2" long. Excellent, $200.00; Mint, $325.00.

PLATE 544. Left: Blue carriage penny toy with rolling wheels and single horse pulling, approx. 2" long. Excellent, $275.00; Mint, $375.00. Right: Green coach tin lithographed penny toy pulled by single horse. Excellent, $300.00; Mint, $400.00.

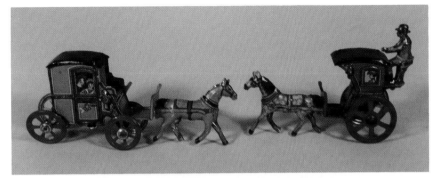

PLATE 545. Penny toy early open roadster #948 tin lithographed rolling automobile, approx. 2½" long. Excellent, $250.00; Mint, $400.00.

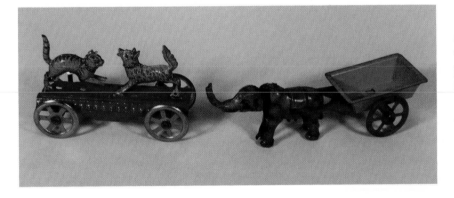

PLATE 546. Left: Cat and dog on wagon tin lithographed rolling penny toy, approx. 2" long. Excellent, $200.00; Mint, $350.00. Right: Elephant pulling cart penny toy. Tin lithographed design, elephant's head bobs up and down; cart rolls. Excellent, $225.00; Mint, $400.00.

PLATE 547. Penny toy Trolley #25 complete with electric connector on top, approx. 2" long. Remarkable tin lithography in excellent detail of passengers inside. Excellent, $300.00; Mint, $475.00.

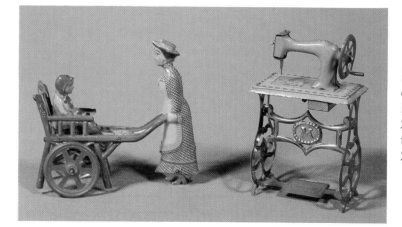

PLATE 548. Left: Mother pushing child in carriage penny toy; feet move, wheels roll. Excellent, $125.00; Mint, $200.00. Right: Sewing machine tin lithographed penny toy with turning machine handle. Excellent, $125.00; Mint, $200.00.

PLATE 549. Punch and Judy Bank, cast iron mechanical featuring brilliant original paint. Excellent, $425.00; Mint, $775.00.

PLATE 550. Speaking Dog cast iron bank with moving arms on girl and "barking" action on dog. Mechanical. Excellent, $1,250.00; Mint, $2,000.00.

PLATE 551. Mason cast iron bank showing figural detail and original paint. Excellent, $2,000.00; Mint, $3,500.00.

PLATE 552. Left: Small gold elephant cast iron still bank. Excellent, $125.00; Mint, $200.00. Right: Large gold/bronze elephant with colorful rider's basket on top, still bank. Excellent, $200.00; Mint, $300.00.

PLATE 553. Saint Bernard rescue dog cast iron bank showing superior die-cast mold detailing. Excellent, $225.00; Mint, $375.00.

PLATE 554. Boxer with red collar cast iron still bank. Excellent, $200.00; Mint, $350.00.

PLATE 555. Prancing horse cast iron still bank with original black finish. Excellent, $200.00; Mint, $300.00.

PLATE 556. Prancing horse with solid base cast iron still bank. Excellent, $175.00; Mint, $250.00.

PLATE 557. Rooster cast iron still bank with original gold and red finish. Excellent, $200.00; Mint, $325.00.

PLATE 558. Mutt and Jeff comic character still bank. Excellent, $400.00; Mint, $575.00.

PLATE 559. Black man in scout-type uniform cast iron still bank. Excellent, $300.00; Mint, $400.00.

PLATE 560. Cast iron gold colored cow still bank. This old gal is complete with udder! Excellent, $125.00; Mint, $200.00.

PLATE 561. Left: Cast iron lion still bank. Excellent, $100.00; Mint, $225.00. Right: Cast iron sitting bear bank. Excellent, $200.00; Mint, $325.00.

PLATE 562. Gold/bronze painted sitting pig still bank. Excellent, $125.00; Mint, $200.00.

PLATE 563. Donkey with saddle and gear cast iron still bank. Excellent, $150.00; Mint, $275.00.

PLATE 564. Cast iron turkey still bank. Excellent, $125.00; Mint, $250.00.

PLATE 565. Cast iron Billiken still bank. Excellent, $150.00; Mint, $300.00.

PLATE 566. Cast iron dog with google eyes still bank showing very colorful paint detailing. Excellent, $150.00; Mint, $325.00.

PLATE 567. Cast iron camel with saddle and rug figural still bank. Excellent, $150.00; Mint, $275.00.

PLATE 568. Left: Cast iron large elephant with rider basket figural still bank. Excellent, $175.00; Mint, $300.00. Right: Cast iron small elephant with rider basket figural still bank. Excellent, $125.00; Mint, $225.00.

PLATE 569. Radio Bank cast iron still bank gives the illusion of being part safe with combination locks and part radio. Excellent, $200.00; Mint, $350.00.

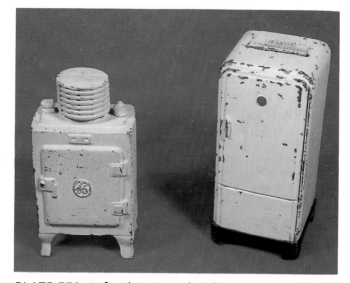

PLATE 570. Left: Electric ice box by G.E. painted still bank, cast iron. Excellent, $225.00; Mint, $350.00. Right: Refrigerator cast iron still bank. Excellent, $150.00; Mint, $250.00.

PLATE 571. White kitten cast iron figural still bank. Excellent, $175.00; Mint, $350.00.

PLATE 572. Dapper Duck cast iron painted figural still bank complete with top hat and umbrella. Caption molded into base says "Save For A Rainy Day." Excellent, $125.00; Mint, $250.00.

PLATE 573. Cast iron Japanese Safe still bank with intricate molded Oriental design features. Excellent, $250.00; Mint, $350.00.

PLATE 576. Cast iron "Red Goose Shoes" still bank premium. Excellent, $125.00; Mint, $225.00.

PLATE 574. Cast iron figural skyscraper still bank. Excellent, $275.00; Mint, $375.00.

PLATE 575. Painted policeman cast iron figural still bank with scowling face and billy club. Excellent, $275.00; Mint, $400.00.

PLATE 577. Left: Tin lithographed semi-mechanical bank. Clown's tongue protrudes to "catch" coin. Excellent, $150.00; Mint, $250.00. Right: Traveler's trunk tin lithographed suitcase still bank. Excellent, $75.00; Mint, $125.00.

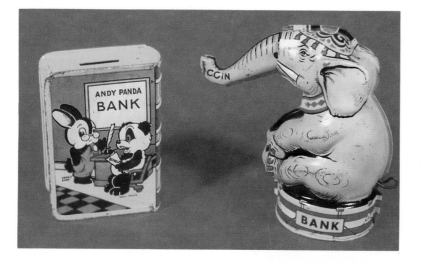

PLATE 578. Left: Andy Panda Bank tin lithographed still bank in book shape. Excellent, $50.00; Mint, $125.00. Right: Circus elephant tin lithographed semi-mechanical bank with lever action. Excellent, $125.00; Mint, $250.00.

PLATE 579. Left: Li'l Abner's Can of Coins tin lithographed bank used as a premium giveaway.   Excellent, $50.00; Mint, $125.00. Right: Benjamin Franklin Thrift Bank with words "The Small Saving Is The Mother Of Thrift." Registering bank. Excellent, $75.00; Mint, $150.00.

PLATE 580. Tin lithographed Dime Bank which registers dimes in amount up to ten dollars. In shape of old cash register. Excellent, $50.00; Mint, $75.00.

PLATE 581. Donald Duck composition character bank by Crown Toy and Novelty with movable jointed head. Excellent, $300.00; Mint, $425.00.

PLATE 582. Jiminy Cricket Pinocchio character wood composition still bank by Crown Toy and Novelty. Excellent, $250.00; Mint, $400.00.

PLATE 583. Left: Porky Pig painted pot metal Warner Brothers character bank by Moss. Excellent, $75.00; Mint, $125.00. Right: Elmer Fudd painted pot metal Warner Brothers bank by Moss. Excellent, $75.00; Mint, $125.00.

PLATE 584. Left: Bugs Bunny by the tree painted pot metal Warner Brothers still bank by Moss. Excellent, $100.00; Mint, $150.00. Right: Bugs Bunny by the barrel painted pot metal figural still bank by Moss. Excellent, $100.00; Mint, $150.00.

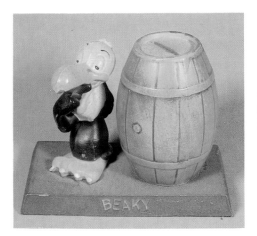

PLATE 585. Beaky the Warner Brothers character painted pot metal still bank by Moss. Excellent, $75.00; Mint, $125.00.

PLATE 586. Lithographed tin clucking, egg-laying chicken windup toy by Baldwin Manufacturing Company. Excellent, $75.00; Mint, $140.00.

PLATE 587. Hobo Train tin lithographed mechanical toy manufactured by Unique Art Manufacturing Company of Newark, New Jersey. Excellent, $275.00; Mint, $400.00.

PLATE 588. Travelchiks mechanical tin lithographed windup car manufactured the Ferdinand Strauss Corporation of New York. Excellent, $350.00; Mint, $500.00.

PLATE 589. Child's tin top manufactured by Chein in the 1930's. Excellent, $40.00; Mint, $80.00.

PLATE 590. J. Chein richly lithographed child's musical chime toy, circa 1920's or 1930's. Excellent, $50.00; Mint, $100.00.

PLATE 591. Cute little kitten tin lithographed sand pail and shovel set. Excellent, $50.00; Mint, $75.00.

PLATE 592. Tin lithographed child's spinning top with unusual vertical shape. Excellent, $50.00; Mint, $75.00.

PLATE 593. Noah's Ark giant tin lithographed sand pail. Excellent, $75.00; Mint, $125.00.

PLATE 594. Children at the beach tin lithographed pail with bright colors and excellent detail. Excellent, $50.00; Mint, $75.00.

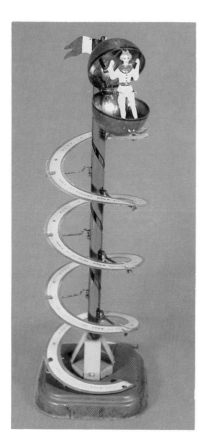

PLATE 595. Mechanical Amusement Toy, early 1900's, rider inside sphere descends upon spiral track. Tin lithographed and painted metal features. Excellent, $700.00; Mint, $900.00.

PLATE 596. Tin lithographed water pump and pail toy with sailboat and fish scenes decorating it. Excellent, $50.00; Mint, $75.00.

PLATE 597. Ornately lithographed child's tin lunch pail with children and dog scenes, circa 1930's. Excellent, $75.00; Mint, $100.00.

PLATE 598. Sand sifter, tin lithographed beach or sand box toy with repeating designs of children on the beach. Excellent, $25.00; Mint, $50.00.

PLATE 599. Easter Bunny pushing the egg cart holiday toy. Extremely colorful tin lithography. Excellent, $50.00; Mint, $90.00.

PLATE 600. Rooster pulling the egg wagon tin lithographed child's toy. Excellent, $50.00; Mint, $90.00.

PLATE 601. Bunny cart tin lithographed 3-wheeled child's Easter toy. Excellent, $65.00; Mint, $100.00.

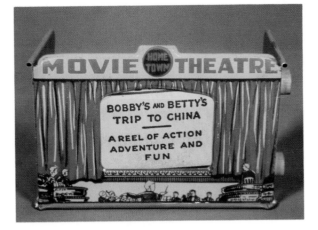

PLATE 602. Home Town Movie Theatre is lithographed tin. Movie "reels" are spools of paper strips. Excellent, $50.00; Mint, $85.00.

PLATE 603. Hopalong Cassidy shooting gallery, with colorful graphics and functional cannon. Lithographed tin, 1950's. Excellent, $125.00; Mint, $200.00.

PLATE 604. Shooting Gallery tin lithographed target toy, featuring big game hunters and targets, 1930's. Excellent, $75.00; Mint, $125.00.

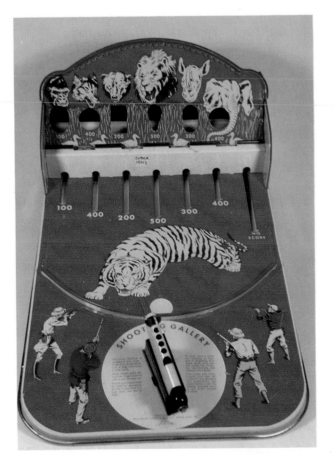

219

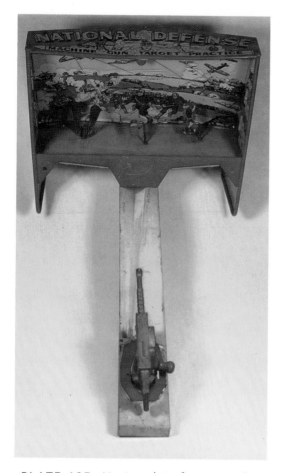

PLATE 605. National Defense machine gun Target Practice lithographed metal target toy. Excellent, $100.00; Mint, $140.00.

PLATE 606. Cast iron and metal Place Kicker mechanical lever action football toy. Excellent, $250.00; Mint, $375.00.

PLATE 607. Coast Defense Gun metal action target toy shown in its original box. Excellent, $60.00; Mint, $95.00.

PLATE 609. Colorful rabbit paper mache composition figural holiday toy. Excellent, $70.00; Mint, $100.00.

PLATE 608. Large black draft horse hollow rubber squeak toy. Excellent, $40.00; Mint, $70.00.

PLATE 610. Carnival chalkware glamour girl with fur coat. Excellent, $30.00; Mint, $50.00.

PLATE 611. Small child's wooden piano with seven keys that actually play and stenciled children's items on front of piano. Excellent, $40.00; Mint, $80.00.

PLATE 612. Unique Dependable Typewriter which can actually be used to print letters. Shown with original box. 1950's. Excellent, $75.00; Mint, $150.00.

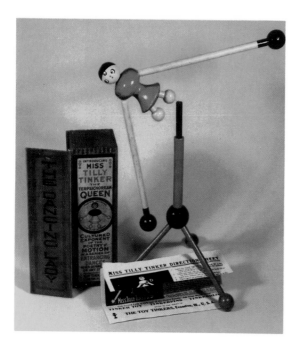

PLATE 613. Miss Tilly Tinker The Terpsichorean Queen early Tinkertoys balancing acrobat toy. Pictured with original colorful shipping box. Excellent, $250.00; Mint, $400.00.

CHAPTER EIGHT

❧ CELLULOID TOYS ❧

Celluloid toys were a short-lived type of toy popular mainly in the 1930's and 1940's, although there was some overlap in the decades just before and after that period.

A forerunner to today's modern vinyls and plastics, celluloid was an unusual chemical concoction of camphor, oils, resins, and hardening agents. It was quick and inexpensive to produce, so it became a popular toy medium especially in the 1930's.

Because celluloid could be injected into a mold and "blown up" when the mold or die was filled with air, most of the common celluloid toys have a rather inflated look. You almost feel that you are holding a little balloon in the shape of a doll or character. This wonderful lightness and smoothness that celluloid brought to toy manufacturing in the 30's and 40's allowed designers to go wild with toy designs and creations.

The pictures leading off this chapter show clearly the diversity of detail on celluloid figural dolls. In Plate 614 it is clear that all of the little celluloid figures are a similar height, and yet detailed design gives each of the toys a strongly individual character. This was because celluloid could be molded into great detail, and most of these Japanese imported toys were painted with incredible detail. These little lightweight toys feel wonderful in the palm of your hand, and their brightly painted detailing makes them extremely pleasing small sculptural pieces.

The lightweight "air-filled" nature of celluloid toys that made them so popular also became the toy's worst enemy. It is remarkable that many of the celluloid toy designs were fashioned into baby rattles or crib toys to be flung about in the crib or baby bed. Considering the gnawing, pounding, throwing, chewing, and gumming that most infant and baby toys take today, it is incredible that any of these examples would have lasted more than a day or two. Some toys manufactured in celluloid were also designed with windup mechanisms (see the chapter in this book on windup toys for celluloid windup examples). A fragile celluloid toy fitted with a tight, active windup mechanism to propel it about the room was bound to self-destruct sooner or later. Thus, celluloid windup toys found in mint condition today were probably never played with a half a century ago. Somebody must have saved them from the curious hands of children.

Even though celluloid figural dolls were highly detailed in themselves, many were often designed with additional accessories. Note the aviator's goggles added to the large aviator doll shown in Plate 617, the cigarette in the mouth of the glamour girl figure in Plate 621, the scout hat in Plate 632, the string reins on the native boy and llama in Plate 637, and the miniature wood golf club in the hand of the sporty little lad in Plate 636. All of these additions only enhance the already superior detailing found on celluloid toys.

Many of the crib toys have rattles inside. Because of the hollow structure of these toys, they make a pleasant sound with something rolling around to rattle inside. Other toys with arms or legs usually joined to the main body with elastic inside were intended to be played with as small dolls. The jointed arms and legs allowed the toys to be posed.

If the fragile nature of celluloid is a drawback to finding superior pieces today, the inexpense of their production helps to compensate, because these were obviously produced by the thousands and so many still exist today. Good celluloid toys still come out onto the market daily, and although some examples are extremely rare, the beginning collector today can usually find an ample amount of mint toys to start or sustain a collection.

As is discussed elsewhere in this book, the paint on many of the best designs of turn of the century tinplate toys is often found in deteriorating condition because it has lost its bond to the metal has over time. Natural adhesives that cause paint to adhere to the metal dry out or break down over time, and thus the paint begins to chip and flake away. It is fortunate for most celluloid toy collectors that they don't have this worry. Because of the smooth, plastic-like nature of the celluloid toys, paints of the 30's and 40's bonded like glue to the surface. Most celluloid toys pictured in this chapter were found by the collectors with paint like new. Notice the wonderful paint finish on the glamour girl in Plate 621, the brilliant colors on Flip the Frog in Plate 628, the rich, warm paint on the cute little bellhop in Plate 635, and the vibrant colors on the cowboys and Indians in Plates 648 and 649.

Some toy collectors specialize in celluloid toys alone, and this is a pleasing angle since the toys all have such a uniform structure and size. It is the variety of sculptural mold, intricate detailing, and artistic painting that gives each toy its special, individual look.

The advent of modern plastics in the early 1950's put an end to celluloid toy production. More durable toys could be made with modern compounds just as inexpensively as with celluloid, so this forerunner of modern plastic compounds slipped into industrial oblivion. But the wonderful surviving celluloid toys are a lasting testimonial to a unique era of toy making that has passed and will never return. In the loving hands of celluloid toy collectors, the toys are safe. They will remain.

PLATE 614. Celluloid figural dolls from the 1930's through the 1940's. Each doll has individual costuming and intricate detail painting. Left: Excellent, $75.00; Mint, $125.00. Center left: Excellent, $200.00; Mint, $275.00. Center right: Excellent, $75.00; Mint, $125.00. Right: Excellent, $100.00; Mint, $200.00.

PLATE 615. Set of four complementary celluloid child dolls holding a puppy, plant, dove and bouquet. Rarely found as a set. Set: Excellent, $200.00; Mint, $400.00.

PLATE 616. The Katzenjammer Kids celluloid character dolls. Hans and Franz, 1930's. Unusual and rarely found together. Excellent, $150.00; Mint, $375.00.

PLATE 617. Left: Small boy aviator celluloid doll figure. Excellent, $100.00; Mint, $200.00. Right: Large aviator doll with jointed arms and separately attached flying goggles. Excellent, $125.00; Mint, $250.00.

PLATE 618. Mama Katzenjammer and the Boys detailed celluloid figural crib toy. Excellent, $450.00; Mint, $575.00.

PLATE 619. Girl tennis player celluloid figural toy with two jointed arms which can be posed, circa 1920's. Excellent, $250.00; Mint, $400.00.

PLATE 621. Glamour Girl exquisitely detailed beauty with cigarette in her mouth. She is also drawing up her negligee on her thigh in a sultry fashion. Probably never intended to be a child's toy. Excellent, $150.00; Mint, $300.00.

PLATE 620. Bathing beauty celluloid figure with bright pink bathing suit and cap. Excellent, $125.00; Mint, $220.00.

PLATE 622. Little girl in red dress figural celluloid doll. She holds a doll in one hand and a baby bottle in the other. Red dress is made of cloth and her arms are jointed. Excellent, $100.00; Mint, $130.00.

PLATE 623. This celluloid policeman's raised hand is mounted on a spring to make it wobble. His glove has "stop" printed on it. His whistle is attached to an actual tiny cord. Excellent design and paint detailing. Excellent, $200.00; Mint, $325.00.

227

PLATE 624. Left: Small Santa Claus figural celluloid crib toy and decoration. Excellent, $65.00; Mint, $100.00. Right: Large Santa figural celluloid rattle. Excellent, $100.00; Mint, $200.00.

PLATE 625. Santa on swan holding a lantern unusual figural celluloid crib toy. Excellent, $150.00; Mint, $325.00.

PLATE 626. Sweet little maid with her fruit basket figural celluloid toy. Excellent, $100.00; Mint, $150.00.

PLATE 627. Boy on an ostrich figural celluloid toy. Excellent, $125.00; Mint, $250.00.

PLATE 628. Flip the Frog early comic character celluloid toy with movable arms. Excellent, $325.00; Mint, $500.00.

PLATE 629. Dapper young gentleman celluloid doll in top hat holding an umbrella in his jointed arm. Excellent, $125.00; Mint, $175.00.

PLATE 630. Harold Lloyd celluloid figural doll with jointed arms, inspired by the comic film star. Excellent, $150.00; Mint, $325.00.

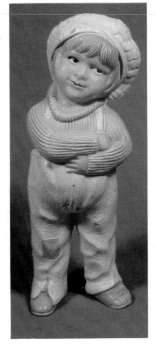

PLATE 631. Street lad celluloid doll in white overalls and pink turtleneck sweater. Excellent, $150.00; Mint, $250.00.

229

PLATE 632. Left: Little Scout celluloid doll holding stick and wearing original hat. Jointed arms. Excellent, $50.00; Mint, $100.00. Right: Little celluloid doll with hands on hips. Excellent, $50.00; Mint, $100.00.

PLATE 633. Left: Comic character celluloid doll figure. Excellent, $75.00; Mint, $125.00. Right: Charlie Chaplin celluloid figural toy. Excellent, $125.00; Mint, $175.00.

PLATE 634. Little pouty baby celluloid crib toy wearing a red night gown. Excellent, $75.00; Mint, $100.00.

PLATE 635. Winking bell hop 1930's figural celluloid doll. Excellent, $150.00; Mint, $300.00.

PLATE 636. Little lad golfer, celluloid figural doll with both arms jointed. Wearing a floppy cap and holding a golf club in one hand and golf ball in the other. Excellent, $275.00; Mint, $400.00.

PLATE 637. Little Boy riding an animal figural celluloid toy. Excellent, $150.00; Mint, $225.00.

PLATE 639. Celluloid doll, probably Little Red Riding Hood with flower basket. Excellent, $100.00; Mint, $150.00.

PLATE 638. Left: Celluloid rabbit. Excellent, $50.00; Mint, $100.00 Right: Celluloid ram, 1930's. Excellent, $40.00; Mint, $80.00.

PLATE 641. Easter Rabbit truck with chicks and bunny celluloid crib toy. Excellent, $75.00; Mint, $125.00.

PLATE 640. Google-eyed dog in derby hat with monocle 1930's or 1940's celluloid figure. Superior hand-painted detailing. Excellent, $300.00; Mint, $400.00.

PLATE 642. Large bull celluloid figure. Excellent, $50.00; Mint, $65.00.

PLATE 643. Celluloid play animal figures. Shown left to right are a bear, lion, elephant, and tiger. Each: Excellent, $30.00; Mint, $50.00.

PLATE 644. Celluloid winter deer in snow white with glitter sparkles on its head and back. Excellent, $25.00; Mint, $50.00.

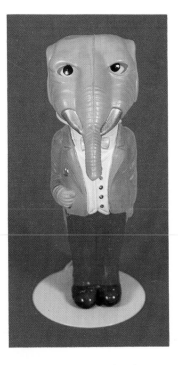

PLATE 646. Elephant Man? This unusual piece has wobbly spring eyes inside head. Celluloid rattle crib toy. Excellent, $100.00; Mint, $150.00.

PLATE 645. Little scotty dog painted in white with shading in hot pink! Excellent, $50.00; Mint, $75.00.

PLATE 647. Rabbit holding carrots. Excellent, $50.00; Mint, $75.00.

PLATE 648. Clockwise from upper left: Celluloid Indian Chief. Excellent, $75.00; Mint, $125.00. Celluloid Indian Boy with jointed arms. Excellent, $125.00; Mint, $200.00. Small Indian Chief with jointed arms. Excellent, $45.00; Mint, $70.00. Two Indians in a celluloid canoe. Excellent, $75.00; Mint, $125.00.

PLATE 649. Left: Celluloid Indian Brave. Excellent, $125.00; Mint, $200.00. Center: Celluloid western horse. Excellent, $125.00; Mint, $175.00. Right: Celluloid cowboy with jointed arms holding two pistols. Excellent, $150.00; Mint, $200.00.

CHAPTER NINE

❧ BOOKS AND PAPER ❧

One of the most appealing areas of children's item collectibles is the field of books and paper. Because published items have been around and plentiful in our society since the beginning of the industrial revolution, today's collectors of children's books and paper collectibles have a wide range and plentiful market of examples to choose from. One of the inventions that made early children's books and paper items have that "vintage" look we find today was the lithograph press. The process printing of this press, known as lithography, produced high color illustrations, book covers, calendar prints, and any item that required a colorful yet delicate design printed onto cardboard or paper.

One of the reasons that Victorian era books and paper items from the children's nursery are so abundant is the fact that families often passed down their complete library of books from generation to generation. Books were easily saved in attics or even in the original old bookshelves, and because they were usually prized with sentiment just because they were books, they were often spared being thrown out.

It is never hard to find examples of pre-1900 children's publications and paper ephemera. Nearly every antique dealer who carries any supply at all of old children's playthings will usually have a stack or two of excellent old books. Many are now nearly one hundred years old!

Probably the best known, most loved, and most prolific publishing company of the Victorian era in the United States was McLoughlin Brothers of New York. The very early and beautifully illustrated soft cover children's picture book illustrated in Plate 650 is a fine example of a McLoughlin Brothers publication. The LITTLE BOYS AND GIRLS ABC book pictured in this color plate is now 110 years old! (It was published in 1884.)

What has helped aid in the longevity of the book illustrated in Plate 650 is the fact that its pages and cover were all printed on a heavyweight, cover stock of fine grade paper. Because of the strength of the printing paper stock, this particular copy has not undergone much of the usual insect damage, wear and tear, and acid deterioration that affects many early printed examples.

Deterioration is an important consideration for the book and paper collector, especially if books older than 50 to 100 years are going to be collected. Because book paper (no matter how heavy) is organic matter, it is eventually going to be subject to biodegrading; that is, the paper will eventually self-destruct. Comic book dealers and collectors have already had to deal with this problem for years since the "golden age" comics of the 1940's were all printed on the very cheapest grades of pulp-type paper to keep costs down. No one published comic books for long life and durability. They were intended to be consumable printed matter . . . kept maybe a few years and then discarded. Now that their organic time clocks are ticking and the acid in the comic paper is starting to destroy the paper from within, comic enthusiasts have had to frantically deal with many of the same preservation techniques that museum curators, archeologists, and scholars have had to deal with for years to preserve historical books and papers that are centuries older. Devoted book and paper enthusiasts are forced to recognize that the life of all book and paper items is inevitably finite and make plans accordingly. The use of acid free archival quality packages and the storing and display of such items in humidity and climate controlled environments can help to retard the processes. With a little tender loving care, collectors can insure that the books that have been around so gracefully since the turn of the century will continue to exist for several more generations.

The Raphael Tuck and Sons Company with centers in New York, London, and Paris was a high quality lithographic publisher just prior to and into the 1900's. The beautiful book cover and illustration of LITTLE RED RIDING HOOD shown in Plates 654 and 655 are examples of the masterful publications by this company. Another fine early 1900's publisher of children's books was the M. A. Donohue Company of Chicago, Illinois. Examples of books by this publisher are the PAINTING AND SKETCHING BOOK pictured in plate 666 and the SANTA CLAUS BIG PICTURE AND STORY BOOK illustrated in Plate 677. Other well-known publishers of early 1900's children's editions were the Saalfield Publishing Company of Ohio, and the D. Lothrop Publishing Company of New York.

One of the first things collectors of Victorian vintage children's books have in common is a love for color. With turn of the century color lithography, the art of children's book illustrations was never more intricate and beautiful. Certainly the publications of today can run rings around the old books in regard to brilliant inks and sharply reproduced graphics, but Victorian era illustrated books by the major publishers using the lithography of the time have a look that can never be repeated. It is partly due to the old inks, the exquisitely detailed lithographic designs that are still today unsurpassed, and partly due to the romance and innocence of the children's illustrations themselves. The books come from an era when the child's volume was a principal form of relaxation, entertainment, and communication between the parent and child. Long before radio, television, stereos, and cassette tape players, parents and children could look forward nightly to the reading hour just before bedtime when all the adventures of the world could be lived through the beautiful old storybooks of the day.

The books and paper toys were kept in the Victorian nursery and dearly loved. Maybe that is why so many have survived. They were cared for and brought along from one generation to the next. Like Peter Pan who follows first Wendy, and then her daughter, the great children's books of the Victorian era now follow the great-grandchildren of the original owners. These printed beauties were once loved and continue to be. Because they are loved, they will survive.

Today's collectors will see to that!

PLATE 650. Little Boys and Girls ABC book, published by McLoughlin Brothers of New York in 1884. Excellent, $75.00; Mint, $125.00.

PLATE 651. Pleasant Hours Painting Book, Father Tuck's Little Artist Series, c. 1900. Excellent, $50.00; Mint, $65.00.

PLATE 652. Little Red Riding Hood Star Rhymes book, early 1900's. Excellent, $35.00; Mint, $50.00.

PLATE 653. Fairy Tale Drawing Book, early 1900's. Excellent, $25.00; Mint, $60.00.

PLATE 654. Little Red Riding Hood, Father Tuck's Fairy Tale Series, by Raphael Tuck and Sons, 1880's. Excellent, $100.00; Mint, $175.00.

"Good Morning Red Riding Hood", said Mr. Wolf.

PLATE 655. Inside illustration of book pictured in Plate 654, published by Raphael Tuck.

PLATE 656. Little Red Riding Hood, Aunt Kate Series picture book published by McLoughlin Brothers, 1899. Excellent, $75.00; Mint, $125.00.

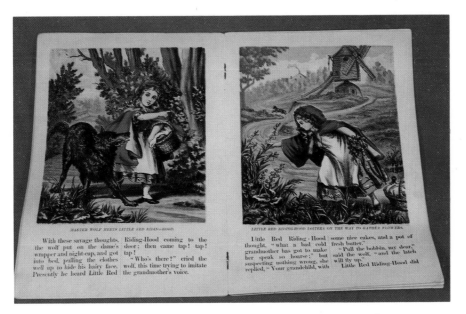

PLATE 657. Inside illustration of book pictured in Plate 656.

PLATE 658. Little Chatterers child's book, Little Chatterwell Series, published by McLoughlin Brothers, c. 1890. Excellent, $35.00; Mint, $50.00.

PLATE 659. Pets ABC book children's alphabet book, 1890's. Excellent, $30.00; Mint, $45.00.

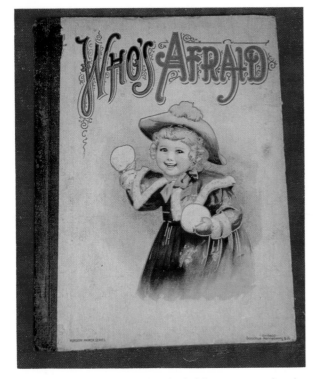

PLATE 660. Who's Afraid children's storybook, circa 1890's. Published by Donohue Henneberry and Company. Excellent, $25.00; Mint, $35.00.

PLATE 661. Sunshine for Little Children storybook, circa 1880's. Excellent, $35.00; Mint, $50.00.

PLATE 662. Father Tuck's Friends in Feather ABC linen book published by Raphael Tuck. Excellent, $20.00; Mint, $45.00.

PLATE 663. Little Miss Muffet and Other Stories by McLoughlin Brothers, copyright 1902. Excellent, $25.00; Mint, $35.00.

PLATE 664. Holiday Fun children's storybook published by McLoughlin Brothers, copyright 1900. Excellent, $20.00; Mint, $30.00.

PLATE 665. Sunny Stories child's linen book, copyright 1903. Excellent, $20.00; Mint, $40.00.

PLATE 666. Painting and Sketching Book published by M. A. Donohue and Company, early 1900's. Excellent, $20.00; Mint, $35.00.

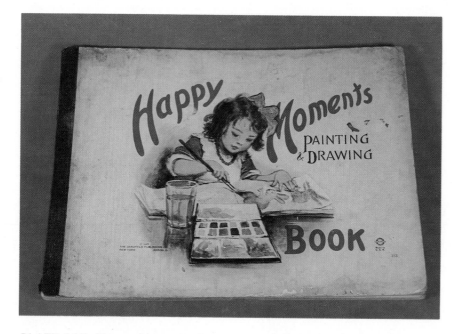

PLATE 667. Happy Moments Painting and Drawing Book, copyright 1925 by Saalfield Publishing. Excellent, $15.00; Mint, $30.00.

PLATE 668. Little Men and Women children's storybook, early 1900's. Excellent, $20.00; Mint, $35.00.

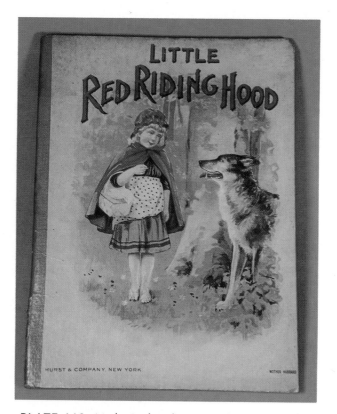

PLATE 669. Little Red Riding Hood, published by Hurst and Company, New York. Excellent, $25.00; Mint, $40.00.

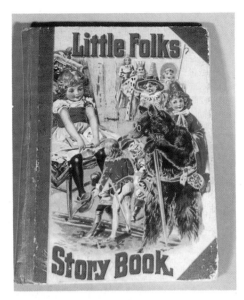

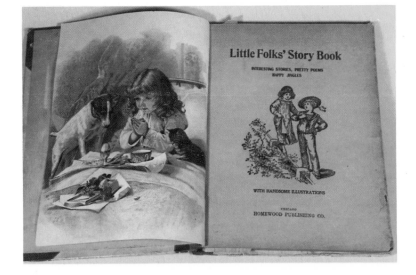

PLATE 670. Little Folks Story Book, published by Homewood Publishing, copyright 1900. Excellent, $15.00; Mint, $35.00.

PLATE 671. Front plate inside color illustration from book pictured in plate 670.

PLATE 673. Inside illustrations from Frances Brundage Little Red Riding Hood book pictured in plate 672.

PLATE 672. Little Red Riding Hood with Frances Brundage illustrations, copyright 1928 by Saalfield Publishing. Excellent, $45.00; Mint, $60.00.

PLATE 674. Mother Goose Paint Book published by Saal-field Publishing of Akron, Ohio, copyright 1908. Excellent, $25.00; Mint, $40.00.

PLATE 675. The Cooking School child's book published by D. Lothrop Company of Boston, copyright 1880. Excellent, $25.00; Mint, $35.00.

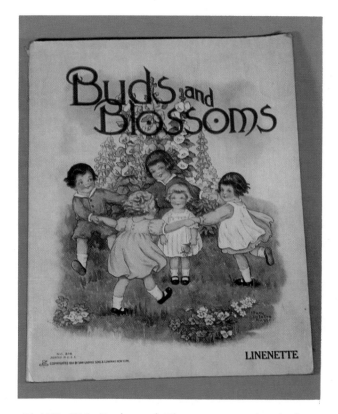

PLATE 676. Buds and Blossoms storybook, linen, copyright 1918 Gabriel and Sons Company. Excellent, $25.00; Mint, $35.00.

PLATE 677. Santa Claus Big Picture and Story Book, published by M. A. Donohue Company, copyright 1925. Excellent, $30.00; Mint, $50.00.

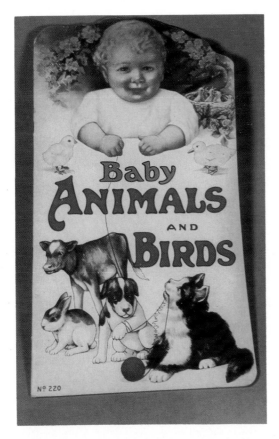

PLATE 678. Baby Animals and Birds illustrated storybook, copyright 1927. Excellent, $25.00; Mint, $35.00.

PLATE 679. The Night Before Christmas illustrated storybook, copyright 1917 by Stecher Lithography. Excellent, $40.00; Mint, $75.00.

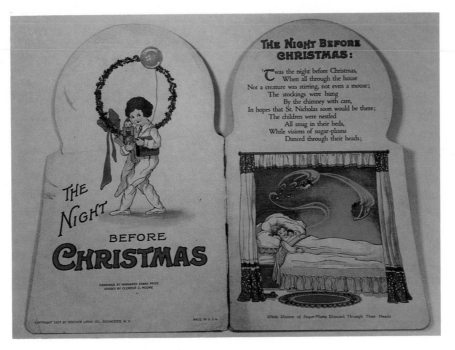

PLATE 680. Illustration for book in plate 679.

PLATE 681. Inside illustration of book in plate 679.

PLATE 682. Red Riding Hood storybook, early 1900's. Excellent, $25.00; Mint, $35.00.

PLATE 683. Boxed picture puzzle published by Milton Bradley. Excellent, $75.00; Mint, $100.00.

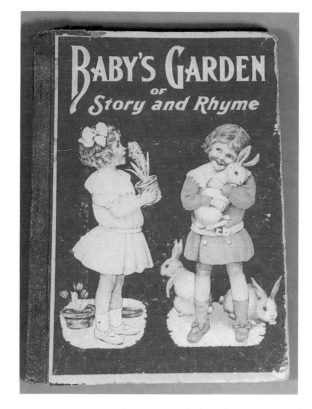

PLATE 684. Baby's Garden of Story and Rhyme, copyright 1917 by John C. Winston Publishers. Excellent, $15.00; Mint, $25.00.

PLATE 685. Puss in Boots published by Saalfield Publishing, copyright 1916. Excellent, $15.00; Mint, $20.00.

PLATE 686. Left: Little Bear and His Friends, copyright 1921 Rand McNally. Excellent, $20.00; Mint, $25.00. Right: Little Bear's Playtime, copyright 1936 Rand McNally. Excellent, $15.00; Mint, $20.00.

PLATE 687. Uncle Wiggily and His Flying Rug, published by Whitman, 1940. Excellent, $15.00; Mint, $20.00.

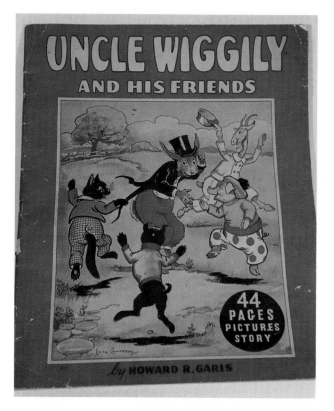

PLATE 688. Uncle Wiggily and His Friends giant picture book, copyright 1933 Whitman. Excellent, $20.00; Mint, $30.00.

PLATE 689. Uncle Tom's Cabin Young Folks Edition published by M. A. Donohue. Excellent, $25.00; Mint, $50.00.

PLATE 690. Pair of Victorian children picture and advertising trade cards, early 1900's. Excellent, $15.00; Mint, $25.00 each.

PLATE 691. Saint Bernard Valentine, early 20th century. Excellent, $15.00; Mint, $30.00.

PLATE 692. Set of four paper and wood "Spool" animals. Set: Excellent, $20.00; Mint, $50.00.

PLATE 693. Baseball valentine, early 20th century.
Excellent, $15.00; Mint, $20.00.

PLATE 694. Puss-in-Boots shoe box,
circa early 1900's. Excellent, $35.00;
Mint, $50.00.

PLATE 695. Buster Brown mechanical valentine.
early 1900's. Excellent, $30.00; Mint, $45.00.

PLATE 696. Girl on toy horse, Victorian
embossed paper figure. Excellent, $35.00;
Mint, $50.00.

PLATE 698. Large horse head paper figure, embossed, early 1900's. Excellent, $20.00; Mint, $40.00.

PLATE 697. Set of three advertising animal cards. Excellent, $10.00; Mint, $20.00 set.

PLATE 699. Star Soap premium children's picture, early 1900's. Excellent, $15.00; Mint, $20.00.

PLATE 700. Garden Days Painting and Drawing Set complete with colorful animal stencils. Excellent, $50.00; Mint, $75.00.

PLATE 701. Garden Days stencil set manufactured by Saalfield, 1920's.

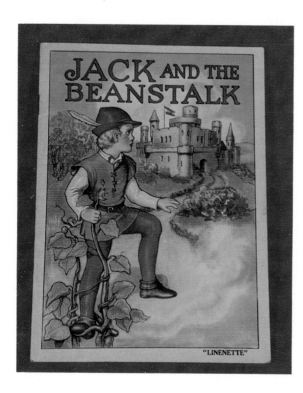

PLATE 702. Jack and the Beanstalk illustrated linenette book, circa 1920's. Excellent, $15.00; Mint, $30.00.

PLATE 703. Set of three Little Red Riding Hood embossed story cards, early 1900's. Excellent, $35.00; Mint, $50.00 set.

PLATE 704. The Merry Pranks of Foxy Grandpa, published by M. A. Donohue, 1905. Excellent, $50.00; Mint, $100.00.

PLATE 705. Buster Brown's Painting Book, early 1900's comic character paint book. Excellent, $65.00; Mint, $120.00.

PLATE 706. Uncle Wiggily Goes Camping book, circa 1940's. Excellent, $15.00; Mint, $20.00.

PLATE 707. Small winking dog mechanical valentine. Excellent, $12.00; Mint, $25.00.

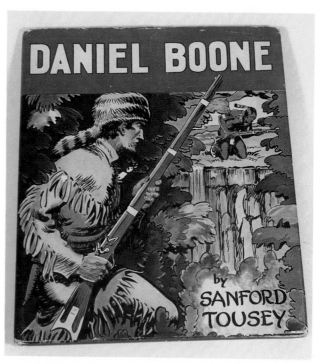

PLATE 708. Little Black Sambo cloth-like book, copyright 1942 by Saalfield. Excellent, $40.00; Mint, $65.00.

PLATE 709. Daniel Boone storybook published by Rand McNally, copyright 1939. Excellent, $20.00; Mint, $40.00.

PLATE 710. The Charlie Chaplin Book, tall linen-like book, circa 1920's. Excellent, $45.00; Mint, $75.00.

PLATE 711. Charlie Chaplin Coloring Book published by Saalfield, 1941. Excellent, $20.00; Mint, $45.00.

PLATE 712. Our Gang Coloring Book, copyright 1933, Saalfield Publishing. Excellent, $35.00; Mint, $55.00.

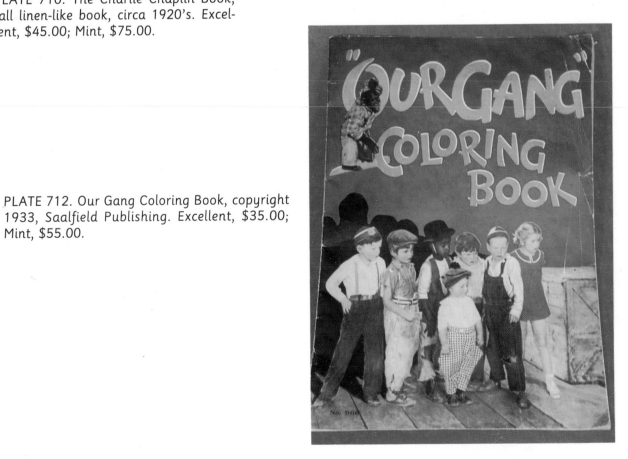

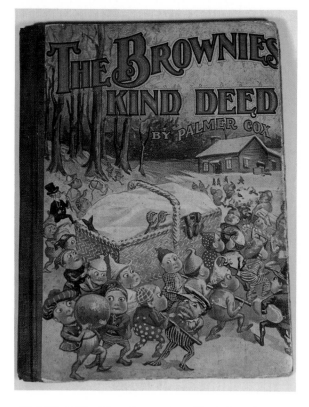

PLATE 713. The Brownies Kind Deed storybook, copyright 1903. Excellent, $50.00; Mint, $75.00.

PLATE 714. Tillie The Toiler comic character book published by Cupples and Leon, copyright 1930. Excellent, $35.00; Mint, $60.00.

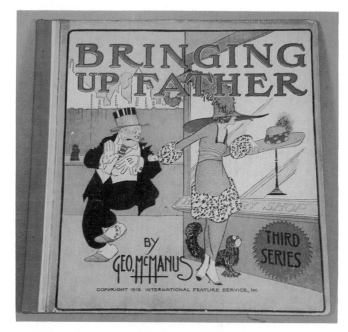

PLATE 715. Bringing Up Father comic character book by Cupples and Leon Publishing, copyright 1919. Excellent, $35.00; Mint, $60.00.

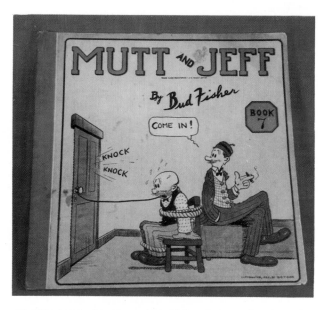

PLATE 716. Mutt and Jeff Book 7, a book published by Cupples and Leon, 1920. Excellent, $35.00; Mint, $60.00.

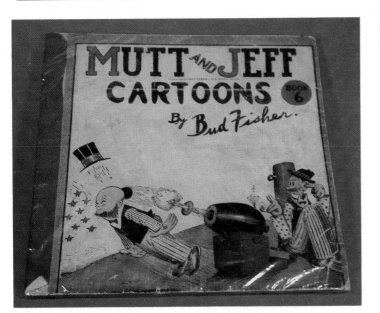

PLATE 717. Mutt and Jeff Book 6 Cupples and Leon book, copyright 1919. Excellent, $35.00; Mint, $60.00.

PLATE 718. Bringing Up Father. Cupples and Leon Publishers, 1919. Excellent, $35.00; Mint, $60.00.

PLATE 719. Smitty At the Ball Game, Cupples and Leon Publishers, copyright 1924. Excellent, $35.00; Mint, $60.00.

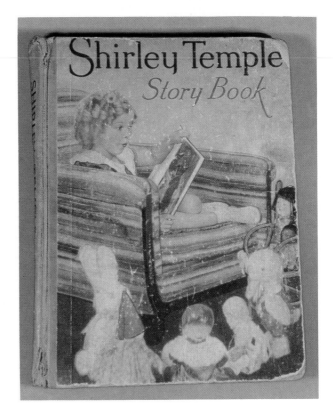

PLATE 720. Shirley Temple Story Book published by Saalfield, copyright 1935. Excellent, $50.00; Mint, $75.00.

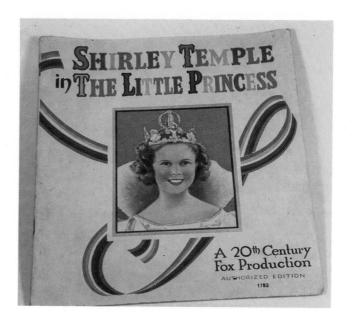

PLATE 722. Shirley Temple In The Little Princess, copyright 1939. Excellent, $35.00; Mint, $60.00.

PLATE 721. Shirley Temple Christmas Book published by Saalfield, copyright 1937. Excellent, $50.00; Mint, $75.00.

PLATE 723. Shirley Temple In Stowaway, copyright 1937 picture book. Excellent, $35.00; Mint, $60.00.

PLATE 724. Shirley Temple in Heidi, copyright 1937 storybook published by Saalfield. Excellent, $50.00; Mint, $75.00.

PLATE 725. Shirley Temple at Play large storybook published by Saalfield, 1935. Excellent, $45.00; Mint, $80.00.

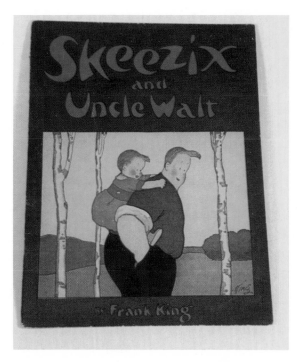

PLATE 726. Skeezix and Uncle Walt book published by Reilly and Lee, copyright 1924. Excellent, $40.00; Mint, $60.00.

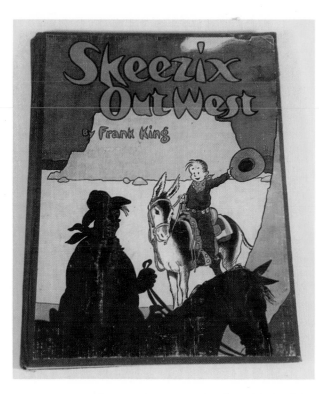

PLATE 727. Skeezix Out West book published by Reilly and Lee, 1928. Excellent, $35.00; Mint, $55.00.

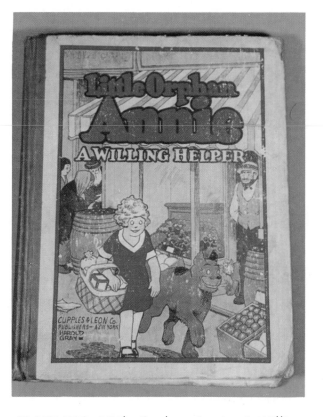

PLATE 728. Little Orphan Annie, A Willing Helper published by Cupples and Leon. Excellent, $35.00; Mint, $60.00.

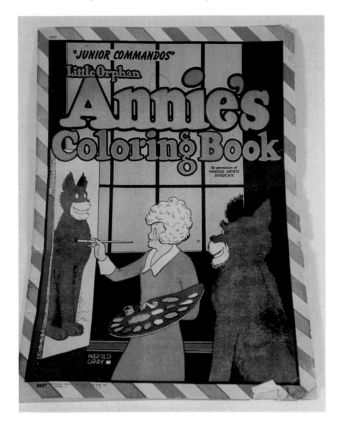

PLATE 729. Little Orphan Annie's Coloring Book, copyright 1943. Excellent, $45.00; Mint, $70.00.

PLATE 730. Little Orphan Annie pop-up book published by Blue Ribbon Books. Excellent, $175.00; Mint, $250.00.

PLATE 731. Little Orphan Annie and the Gooneyville Mystery, Better Little Books, by Whitman. Excellent, $20.00; Mint, $40.00.

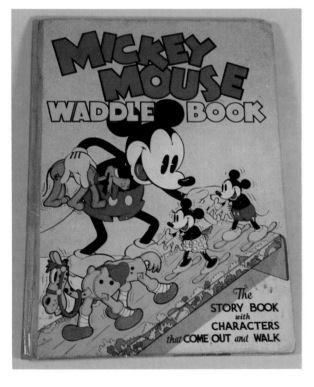

PLATE 732. Mickey Mouse Waddle Book by Blue Ribbon Books, copyright 1934. Excellent, $900.00; Mint, $1,800.00.

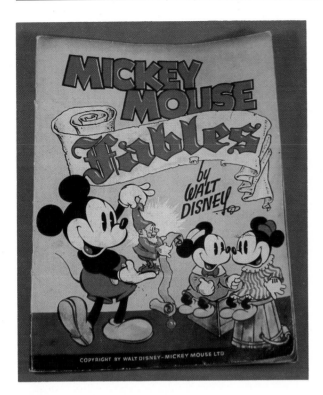

PLATE 733. Mickey Mouse Fables book published in England. Excellent, $75.00; Mint, $150.00.

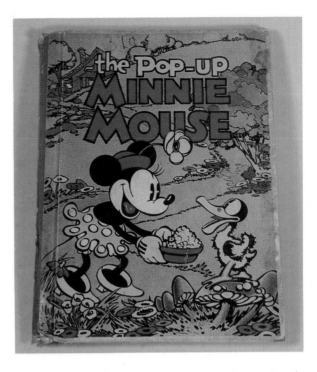

PLATE 734. The Pop-Up Minnie Mouse Book with three inside pop-up pages, c. 1930's Walt Disney Enterprises. Excellent, $150.00; Mint, $250.00.

PLATE 735. Donald Duck storybook, 1930's, copyright Walt Disney Enterprises. Excellent, $70.00; Mint, $100.00.

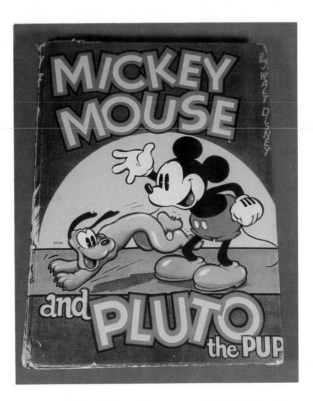

PLATE 736. Mickey Mouse and Pluto The Pup hardcover storybook, 1930's c. Walt Disney Enterprises. Excellent, $100.00; Mint, $175.00.

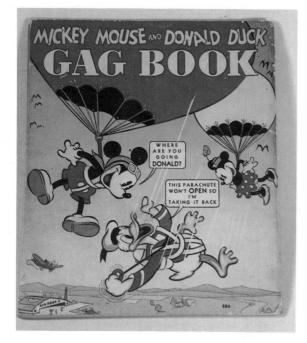

PLATE 737. Mickey Mouse and Donald Duck Gag Book, 1930's, Walt Disney Enterprises. Excellent, $125.00; Mint, $175.00.

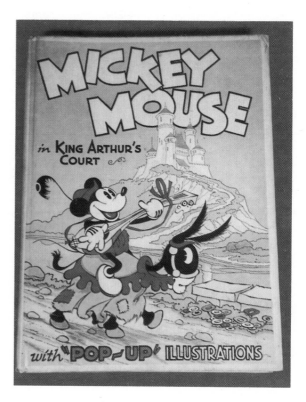

PLATE 738. Mickey Mouse in King Arthur's Court, published by Blue Ribbon Books, c. Walt Disney, 1933, a pop-up book. Excellent, $250.00; Mint, $400.00.

PLATE 739. Walt Disney's Pinocchio Picture Book, c. 1939 Walt Disney Enterprises. Excellent, $75.00; Mint, $125.00.

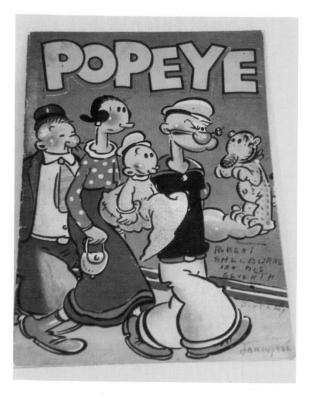

PLATE 740. Popeye linen-like book, copyright 1937. Excellent, $50.00; Mint, $75.00.

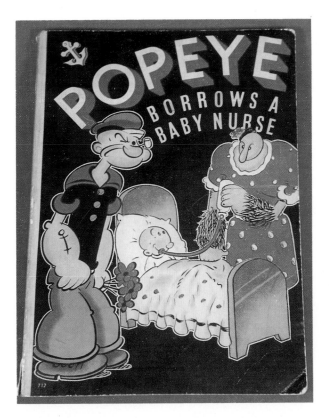

PLATE 741. Popeye Borrows a Baby Nurse, published by Whitman in 1937. Excellent, $120.00; Mint, $150.00.

PLATE 742. Scootles in Kewpieville color book by Rose O'Neill and published by Saalfield in 1936. Excellent, $100.00; Mint, $150.00.

PLATE 743. Moon Mullins Crayon and Paint Book, published by McLoughlin Brothers, copyright 1932. Excellent, $35.00; Mint, $65.00.

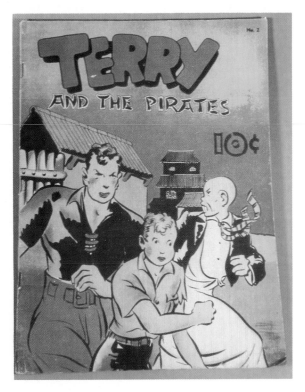

PLATE 744. Terry and the Pirates Book, published by Dell and copyright 1937. Excellent, $20.00; Mint, $35.00.

PLATE 745. The Pop-Up Buck Rogers, published by Blue Ribbon Books, copyright 1935. Excellent, $150.00; Mint, $275.00.

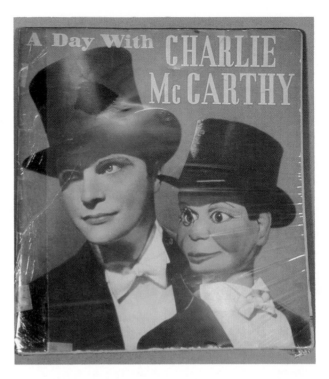

PLATE 746. A Day With Charlie McCarthy, storybook copyright 1939. Excellent, $35.00; Mint, $60.00.

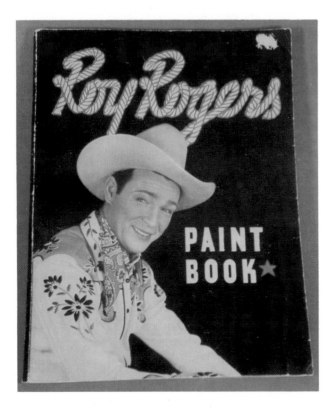

PLATE 747. Roy Rogers Paint Book, published by Whitman in 1944. Excellent, $25.00; Mint, $50.00.

PLATE 748. Raggedy Ann and Andy Coloring Book published by Saalfield in 1944. Excellent, $75.00; Mint, $90.00.

PLATE 749. Blondie Paint Book published by Whitman in 1947. Excellent, $25.00; Mint, $35.00.

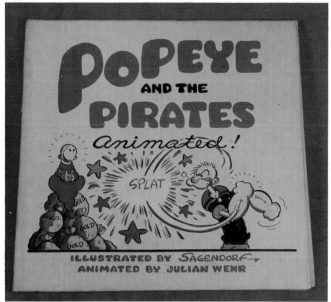

PLATE 750. Popeye and the Pirates Animated book published by Duenwald Printing Corp. in 1945. Excellent, $150.00; Mint, $200.00.

PLATE 751. Barney Google book published by Saalfield in 1935. Excellent, $35.00; Mint, $45.00.

PLATE 752. Bugs Bunny Porky Pig Paint Book published by Whitman in 1946. Excellent, $25.00; Mint, $40.00.

PLATE 753. Lil' Abner and Daisy Mae coloring book, copyright 1951. Excellent, $35.00; Mint,

PLATE 754. Howdy Doody character puzzle, 1950's. Excellent, $15.00; Mint, $30.00.

PLATE 755. Howdy Doody Wonder Bread premium paper puppet. Excellent, $35.00; Mint, $60.00.

PLATE 756. "It's Howdy Doody Time" puzzle, 1950's. Excellent, $25.00; Mint, $50.00.

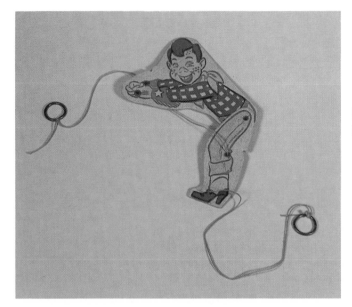

PLATE 757. Howdy Doody cardboard climbing puppet, 1950's. Excellent, $25.00; Mint, $40.00.

PLATE 758. Howdy Doody Sticker Fun book, published by Whitman in the 1950's. Excellent, $25.00; Mint, $50.00.

PLATE 759. Howdy Doody and the Air-O-Doodle record set by RCA Victor, 1950's. Excellent, $20.00; Mint, $45.00.

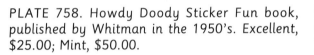

➣ TOY NETWORKING ➣

Beginning collectors often come up to me and in the course of conversation nearly always ask me "where did you get all of your toys?" There's no mystique about it, really. I got my toys by seeking out every lead and attending nearly every show within a reasonable distance of my home, one every weekend. That's the way nearly everybody gets their toys. But it's not the only way.

Aside from being an author and a collector, I am also a teacher and a theater director. One of my former students made her debut on Broadway last season in "Will Rogers' Follies" and needless to say I was as proud of her as if she had been my own child when I visited and dined with her in New York City. She's only 24, one year out of college, and already performing on the Great White Way. When I asked her how she was able to launch her career so quickly, she explained that she used the method of "networking." That is, every waking moment of every single day, she never misses a chance to meet a new director, talk with an agent, attend every audition, and get her name out in every circle around town. She explained that much of an actor's success in the profession hinged upon to ability to sell your talents to the right buyers and to keep all doors open.

As I walked through Times Square full of enthusiasm after our reunion and proud of her successes, I thought to myself that this whole idea of "networking" has been used in the business world and entertainment industry for years, but nobody has paid much attention to its application to collecting. I know collectors out there who are continually frustrated during the "down times" when there are no toy shows around to attend. I know other resourceful collectors who make it a challenge to insure that something for their collection arrives via the UPS truck weekly, sometimes daily. So what separates the frustrated collector from the resourceful one? Networking. As my young actress friend has already learned, life is too short to let opportunities pass by. You have to be ready for the "big break" at any moment. And the way to insure that those breaks come your way is to get yourself into the toy collecting "network."

The first place to start is to "activate your file" as they would say in the professional world. Let people out there know who you are and what you collect. First assignment: Place attractive ads in every toy publication classified section or marketplace that you can find. Be specific about who you are and what you want to buy. Don't mention prices in ads. Leave all that open for negotiation, that way nobody's hands are tied. If personal security is a concern, get a post office box for mail correspondence. It is surprising how much interesting mail repeating ads will generate. This may be an obvious tactic, but don't overlook or underestimate it.

Second assignment for the toy collector entering the "network": Get a business card, or collector card depending upon your approach. State all the particulars about how to contact you (especially day and evening phone numbers) and exactly what it is you collect or are looking for. My own collection of business cards of toy collectors is more useful to me than any yellow pages. These are the people who help me find toys all year long. Leave your card with toy dealers at shows when you make a personal contact. Pass through an antique mall with a dealer who sells what you collect? Leave your card at the front desk of the mall and ask that dealer to contact you. You may never pass that way again, but the phone lines do and you can let UPS make return trips for you.

Assignment Three: Make want lists. Everybody talks about them, but how many have you ever ACTU-ALLY SEEN? Sit down on a rainy day and do some dreaming. List exactly what you are looking for and explain that you are always willing to negotiate prices. Drop these by every local dealer in your area that deals in toys and get them into the hands of even general antique dealers who do not specialize in toys. Some of my best toy deals in the past twenty years have been with general line antique dealers who didn't share in my passion for playthings and were more than happy to "flip" a toy (their lingo for turning a toy over quickly at a small profit rather than dragging it around for two years waiting for the top dollar). Don't overlook these guys. You can get some wonderful deals this way.

Assignment Four: Read. Read everything you can get your hands on when it comes to toys. Reading magazines such as Toy Trader, Antique Toy World, and The Inside Collector, is the perfect start. Read toy magazines and auction circulars and leave no piece of printed matter unturned. Aside from seeing new ads from other people and upcoming auctions, reading will make you knowledgeable so that you can deal comfortably with the new inquiries and contacts that your "networking" will generate. Don't underestimate the potential of "left bids" or phone bids in general auctions. If you see something interesting in a listing, call about it. Nine out of ten auctioneers will be more than obliging to you with toy descriptions and be glad to bid for you as an absentee with a "left bid." A few auctioneers don't like to deal with phone bids because they may have gotten stung a few times. Be understanding. If they don't allow absentee bids, they probably have a good reason from past experiences.

Assignment Five: Get a home computer. If you already have one, get a modem (these allow your phone to communicate with other databases around the country). I don't own a modem, but I do know several very resourceful collectors who have snagged up a few toys that appeared in SWAP listings of specialized databases. The best place to seek out these computer classifieds is through the specialized toy collector trade publications for such things as Disneyana, scale model trains, animation art, etc. Be patient. This is a new area and is highly experimental, but the immediacy of a toy listing coming "on line" just when your system is switched on churns up futuristic visions of a virtual in-home Wall Street for toy collectors. We are not there yet, but...soon. For those who don't have or use a modem but do have the home computer, build your TOY CONTACT DATABASE. List every name, every dealer, every human being that you know on this earth who might be useful to you in your quest for toys. When you have all the information stored neatly inside, have your printer spit it all back out in the form of mailing labels. (If you have never done this with your home computer, it is high time you learned.) When the labels are printed, do a mass maling! Stuff in your want lists, anything you might have available for trade, and maybe a particularly grabbing extra flyer reserved just for that one toy you are looking for! You may be quite surprised at the response. If nothing else, at least everybody on your list will be thinking about you on the day they get your mailing. That, in itself, will help to "activate" you on the network.

Assignment Six: BE A STAR! I know this one sounds crazy, but don't overlook the power of the media. That's right, radio, TV, and papers. I'm not suggesting that anybody actually advertise through the electronic media that you will buy old toys. I've always been curious about the potential results, but I don't think the bottom line would be cost effective. What you can do is write up a little press release. It doesn't have to be anything fancy. Send it out to your local paper telling them who you are, and what might be interesting to the general public about your toy collection. You'd be surprised how receptive a local editor might be on a slow day. Tell them what's unusual about your collection, how you started, and assure them that you've got some toys for them to photograph. (They're especially receptive to stories about old toys around Christmas.) Dash your release off to local radio and TV stations with talk shows and tell them you'd love to be a guest on a phone-in. Old toys are generally interesting to everybody, and if anybody would just "happen" to have something to sell that you are looking for, they can contact you care of the station. And with the advent and increasing popularity of public access local cable programming, it is now very possible to get you and your toys on television. (If your town is very small and everybody knows you and where you live, I wouldn't pursue this avenue because of security reasons. If you must, make sure that you don't broadcast to the world that your collection is worth something like several hundred thousand dollars.)

Through the use of business cards, advertising, interviews, databases, computer modem linkups, labels, mass mailings, want lists, personal contacts and visits to local dealers, aggressive reading of periodicals and auction listings, and press releases, you can get your name "out there" on the network, nationally. For a small investment and some creativity, you can expand your toy horizons far beyond normal expectations. If it's a goal to get those great toys arriving on your doorstep during the "down times," then it's time to be resourceful.

And like my young actress friend, a little creative networking can go a long way. Maybe it won't get you to Broadway, but it might help you find some wonderful old toys.

Go ahead. "Activate" yourself. Get on the network. The toy world is waiting to hear from you!

COLLECTOR RESOURCES

The field of antique toy collecting is growing and the intensity of these toy enthusiasts is overwhelming. Many publications and auction catalogs are available for those wishing to acquire antique toys through the mail. The following are publications that contain valuable information on a variety of antique toy topics.

THE INSIDE COLLECTOR
P.O. Box 98
Elmont, NY 11003

TOY BOX
Dept. TB
8393 E. Holly Road
Holly, MI 48442

COLLECTORS SHOWCASE
P.O. Box 837
Tulsa, OK 74101

TOY TRADER
P.O. Box 1050
Dubuque, IA 52004

ANTIQUE TOY WORLD
P.O. Box 34509
Chicago, IL 60634

The following are reputable mail and phone bid auction houses that deal in antique toys.

HAKE'S AMERICANA
&
COLLECTIBLES
P.O. Box 1444
York, PA 17405
(717) 848-1333

SMITH HOUSE TOY SALES
P.O. Box 336
Eliot, ME 03903
(207) 439-4614

ROBERT COUP
P.O. Box 348
Leola, PA 17603
(717) 656-7780

A MOUSE IN THE HOUSE
VINTAGE DISNEYANA
P.O. Box 2183
Clarksville, IN 47129

BERTOIA AND BRADY AUCTIONS
2413 Madison Ave.
Vineland, NJ 08360

'TIQUES
7 Rittner Lane
Old Bridge, NJ 08857

RICHARD OPFER AUCTIONEERING
1919 Greenspring Drive
Timonium, MD 21093

NEW ENGLAND AUCTION GALLERY
P.O. Box 2273
W. Peabody, MA 01960-7273
(503) 535-3140

About The Author

David Longest

David Longest was a toy collector for eight years before he ever thought about writing articles for toy magazines or writing books. A teacher by profession and a theatre director for the love of it, Longest began to moonlight by writing toy articles for such publications as ANTIQUE WEEK, Collector's Showcase, and Antique Toy World. He has also been a contributor to the new Inside Collector magazine and is currently a contributing editor for Toy Trader magazine where he writes a monthly column "On the Toy Trail," produces their monthly "Dealer Talk" series, and serves as reviewer for all toy publications. He has also been a guest lecturer on antique toys.

This present book marks Longest's fifth title published by Collector Books in the past ten years, where all five of his books on toys are still in print. His first two books were Character Toys and Character Toys and Collectibles–Series Two. A later book, Toys, Antique and Collectible is an all encompassing paperback antique toy price guide with over 10,000 toy entries. His fourth work, The Collector's Encyclopedia of Disneyana was co-authored with Michael Stern in 1992.

Longest's love of all antique toys is shared with his wife, Ann, who collects turn of the century Victorian toys, teddy bears, and nursery toys. The author's main toy collecting specialty is 1930s vintage Disneyana. He has been a toy collector for eighteen years. His seven year old daughter, Claire, has helped him on more than one occasion to find some great toys "under the table."

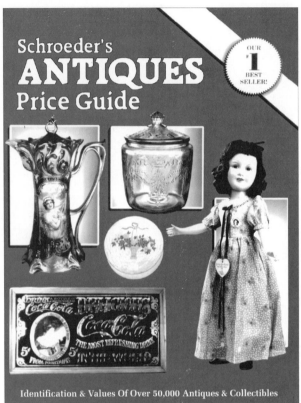